Somatic Therapy Exercises for Beginners

A 28-Day Guide to Stress Relief, Anxiety Management, Weight Loss, Chronic Pain Alleviation, Digestive Health, and Mind-Body Balance in Just 10 Minutes a Day with Simple Techniques and Interactive Worksheets

By

Eva Greenleaf

Contents

Introduction – Exploring Somatic Therapy

Somatic therapy refers to a variety of treatments that focus on the connection between the mind and the body. The word "somatic" means "related to the body." A somatic therapist uses special techniques to help release trauma that has become "stuck" in the body. This therapeutic approach works by addressing the ongoing interaction between the mind and the body, and incorporates elements of psychotherapy to make the healing process smoother.

Somatic therapists believe that negative emotions, like emotions experienced during a traumatic event, can get stuck in the body. If these emotions are not released, they can lead to psychological issues or physical problems like chronic neck or back pain.

Somatic therapists use a variety of techniques and somatic exercises to help release the tension and stress trapped in your body. These methods aim to improve both your emotional and physical well-being. Some of the techniques used include:

Breathing Exercises

- These help to calm the mind and relax the body. Mental focus and breath control can help release tension and improve your sense of peace.

Body Awareness

- This technique helps you become more conscious of your body's sensations. By paying attention to these sensations, you can begin to understand where your body holds stress and learn ways to release it.

Meditation

- This practice helps you become more aware of your body and mind. It encourages relaxation and can help you process, and release pent-up emotions.

Movement and Dance

- Physical movement can help release stored tension and improve your emotional state. Dance, yoga, and other forms of movement allow you to express feelings that may be difficult to put into words.

Somatic exercises offer several benefits by focusing on the body. They help individuals become more aware of their physical sensations and how these relate to their emotions. This increased awareness can lead to better emotional regulation and overall well-being.

Somatic therapy also addresses the interconnectedness of the mind and body, promoting holistic healing. It encourages individuals to listen to their bodies and understand the signals they are receiving. This approach can lead to a more balanced and healthy life.

The Fundamentals and Core Principles of Somatic Therapy

Somatic therapy, although a relatively new technique in the therapy field, has found its roots among the most effective therapies recommended by therapists. Its methods differ from traditional therapy, and this is what makes it unique as well as effective. A somatic therapist employs various techniques to assist in the release of trauma or negative emotions from the body. These techniques include:

Body awareness: This initial step involves learning to identify and acknowledge areas of tension within the body while also recognizing calming thoughts and sensations.

Grounding: The practice of grounding involves establishing a deep connection with both the body and the earth. This is achieved through sensory awareness of the body and its connection to the ground; this technique ultimately calms the nervous system.

Resourcing: Patients are encouraged to recall sources of safety and comfort in their lives, such as supportive relationships, personal strengths, or cherished memories. By evoking positive feelings associated with these resources, individuals establish emotional stability and resilience.

Pendulation: During this technique, the therapist guides the patient from a state of relaxation to one similar to the traumatic experience. This process may be repeated, allowing the release of pent-up energy. Despite potential discomfort or anxiety, the patient is gently guided back to a relaxed state. This helps the client gradually learn how to achieve relaxation independently.

Titration: The therapist assists the patient in revisiting a traumatic memory while observing any bodily changes that occur. Addressing physical sensations as they arise is an integral part of this technique.

Sequencing: This technique involves close observation of the consecutive release of tension from the body. For example, tension may initially manifest as tightness in the chest before spreading to the throat, followed by a sensation of shaking as the tension disperses.

These techniques serve to facilitate the gradual release and processing of stored trauma and negative emotions, empowering individuals to cultivate a greater sense of well-being and resilience.

Although Somatic therapy is primarily aimed towards treating stress and trauma in the body, its calming technique can also help an individual with the following mental health problems:

- Grief
- Anger
- Anxiety
- Depression
- Trust
- Intimacy
- Insecurity

Somatic therapy is a feild that is still growing. However, there are some common techniques and therapies which people use; these are listed below:

Somatic experiencing addresses the body's responses to trauma. Some therapists may encourage discussion of traumatic experiences, while others focus only on describing the physical sensations experienced during the sessions. Patients may be guided through movements that activate negative emotions, enabling the safe release of pent-up energy and slow desensitization to triggers.

Neurosomatic therapy targets patients whose symptoms lean toward the physical end of the mind-body range. This technique identifies core sources of tension and physical discomfort in the nervous system and body. Techniques such as massage, posture correction, and targeted exercises are used to address imbalances and ease symptoms.

EMDR therapy involves recalling traumatic experiences in brief intervals while simultaneously concentrating on an external stimulus, such as eye movements, hand tapping, or auditory cues.

Hakomi therapy emphasizes mindfulness, fostering an atmosphere of non-judgmental awareness for the present moment. Therapists assist patients in identifying bodily signals of unconscious beliefs, enabling the quick exploration and safe release of unconscious trauma.

Sensorimotor psychotherapy integrates elements of psychotherapy, somatic therapy, attachment theory, and neuroscience, as well as techniques from Hakomi therapy. This approach enables patients to safely revisit traumatic events, complete unresolved actions from these experiences, and get a sense of closure.

Stored Experiences – An Insight into Your Personal History and Trauma

The concept of somatic therapy views the mind and body as intrinsically linked parts of the same body. A common belief for the practitioners of this school of thought is that the mind and body both store trauma, and it becomes trapped inside. This can have a negative effect on a person's health, as well as their mental state.

Somatic therapy is a relatively new form of healing in the West. However, the results speak for themselves. Somatic therapy has introduced many exercises and concepts that help release the pent-up energy inside the body. It is a therapy technique designed to help you heal on a fundamental level.

A huge reason for this pent-up stress inside your body is because of the release of cortisol. It is a stress hormone released when you encounter trauma, raising blood sugar and blood pressure levels, ultimately weakening the immune system.

Constant stress can cause physical symptoms. Furthermore, some negative experiences can instill deeply ingrained beliefs that are inaccessible to our conscious minds. These may include thoughts such as "I am a bad person" or "I will never be successful," which are both negative and unhelpful.

This trauma is not just a one-time occurrence and can resurface again and again, causing the individual to experience stress repeatedly. This trauma becomes so ingrained in the individual's mind that any stressful situation may trigger it easily, causing damage to both the physical and mental state of the individual. However, research into somatic therapy has shown promising results in healing these traumatic wounds.

"Somatic experiencing" is a type of somatic therapy that was conducted in a research study. Several people with PTSD participated in this study, showing significant results, as their symptoms of PTSD and depression were shown to improve. It was concluded that the reason behind their PTSD symptoms manifesting again and again was stress activation.

PTSD is different from exposure therapy; unlike exposure therapy, PTSD requires the recount of the traumatic incident in detail. Somatic experiencing does not support this practice. Instead, the clients are asked to think about their traumatic incident and recount their feelings of stress. Then, they are guided to lower this stress trigger through body exercises and breathing techniques.

Another study called **eye movement desensitization and reprocessing (EMDR)** has been recommended by many mental healthcare experts, which helps to reduce stress and trauma. This technique calls for the patient to recall their trauma while moving their eyes from left to right rapidly. This is a simple technique that takes only 5-10 minutes of practice daily, and this movement can help unlock the hidden feelings of stress and unprocessed memories of the incident and alleviate physical symptoms.

A 2014 review found substantial evidence supporting the effectiveness of EMDR therapy in treating emotional trauma and other negative life experiences. The review revealed that seven out of ten studies showed EMDR therapy produced positive outcomes more rapidly than trauma-focused cognitive behavioral therapy (CBT).

Hands-on Practice – Interactive Learning Worksheets and Exercises

Somatic hands-on practice exercises encourage mindful movement and body awareness, promoting physical and mental well-being.

To further support these exercises, worksheets and other physical exercises can be a valuable supplement. These may include guided prompts for tracking progress, detailed descriptions of exercises, and reflective questions to deepen body awareness. They can also provide planned routines, ensuring that your somatic exercise routine is balanced and complete. By incorporating these worksheets into your exercise practice, you can maintain consistency and focus, making it easier to incorporate the principles of somatic exercises and movement in daily life. Worksheets can offer tips for proper alignment and breathing techniques, enhancing the effectiveness of each exercise.

The following exercises and worksheets will do just that, providing additional support for your physical, mental, and emotional healing.

Breath Work Exercise

4-7-8 Breathing Technique

The 4-7-8 breathing technique is a simple and powerful exercise designed to promote relaxation and stress reduction. It can be practiced anywhere, and you only need 10 minutes daily to perform it, making it a perfect tool for managing stress and promoting calmness.

Steps:

- Sit in a comfortable position. Ensure your back is straight and your hands are resting in your lap, or at your sides. Close your eyes to help focus your attention.

- Begin by exhaling through your mouth, making a whooshing sound as you empty your lungs fully.

- Close your mouth and inhale through your nose while counting to four. Feel your stomach and chest expand as you fill your lungs with air.

- Hold your breath for a while, counting to seven. This will allow the oxygen to fully circulate throughout your body, promoting a sense of calm.

- Exhale through your mouth while counting to eight. Focus on pushing out as much air as possible from your lungs.

- This completes one cycle. Repeat the process for four cycles. Over time, you can increase the number to eight as you become more comfortable with the technique.

Benefits:

- The extended exhaling helps the parasympathetic nervous system to relax the body, and reduce fight-or-flight response.

- Counting and controlled breathing helps clear the mind, improving mental clarity and focus.

- Practicing this technique before bedtime can calm the mind and prepare the body for restful sleep.

- The inhaling and exhaling strengthen the lungs and improve overall respiratory efficiency.

- This breathing exercise can lower blood pressure, and improve heart health by decreasing stress and promoting relaxation.

Mindful Walking Exercise

Mindful walking is a practice that promotes awareness and calmness while walking, allowing you to connect more deeply with your surroundings and inner experiences. Here's a step-by-step 10 minute guide to a mindful walking exercise:

Preparation:

- Select a quiet and safe outdoor or indoor space where you can walk without distractions. It could be a park, garden, beach, or a quiet path.

- Before you begin, set an intention for your mindful walk. This could be to encourage gratitude, release stress, or connect with nature.

Steps:

- Start walking at a comfortable pace, and pay attention to the sensation of each step and notice the contact of your feet with the ground or floor.

- As you walk, pay attention to your breathing pattern. Feel the rhythm of your breathing and the natural flow of inhales and exhales.

- Tune into your senses as you walk. Notice the sights, sounds, smells, and sensations around you. Observe the colors, shapes, and textures in your environment without judgment.

- Pay attention to your body's physical sensations as you move. Notice the movement of your muscles, the shifting of your weight, and any areas of tension or relaxation.

- Whenever you start to get distracted, remind yourself of your sorroundings, maintaining your focus and the experience of walking. Use your breath as an anchor to keep you grounded.

- As you walk, encourage a sense of gratitude for the ability to move and experience the world around you. Appreciate the beauty in your surroundings.

- Continue walking mindfully for a duration that feels comfortable to you. Allow yourself to be fully present and open to whatever happens during the walk.

Benefits:

- Mindful walking can help reduce stress and promote relaxation by encouraging a state of present-moment awareness.

- Practicing mindful walking enhances your sensory awareness and helps you connect more deeply with your surroundings.

- By focusing on the present moment, mindful walking can clear the mind and improve mental focus, leading to better decision-making and problem-solving.

- Regular mindful walking practice can contribute to overall well-being, nurturing a sense of peace, contentment, and connection to oneself and the world.

- Mindful walking provides physical exercise and can be a gentle way to stay active and maintain mobility and balance.

Guided Imagery Worksheet

Guided imagery is a powerful method that uses the imagination to create a sense of relaxation, focus, and inner peace. Given ahead is a guided imagery worksheet which can help you rejuvenate in your journey to a healthy body and mind.

Step 1: Preparation

Find a quiet place where you can relax without interruptions. Keep your eyes closed as you sit or lie down in a comfortable position. Take a few slow, deep breaths, inhaling through your nose and exhaling through your mouth. With each breath you take, feel you body relax. Make a conscious effort to let go of any tensions or stress you may be holding onto.

Step 2: Setting the Scene

Imagine yourself standing at the edge of a calm lake, surrounded by green trees and beautiful flowers. Feel the sun on your skin and the breeze in the air. Visualize the blue water of the lake, reflecting the sky above. Listen to the sounds of nature around you— the chirping of birds, the rustling of leaves, the waves of water.

What kind of feeling does this evoke in you?

_____

_____

_____

_____

Step 3: Exploration

Begin to walk slowly along the edge of the lake, feeling the ground beneath your feet. Take in the beauty of your surroundings—the colors, the textures, the fragrances. Pause to admire a flower or a butterfly. Feel a sense of peace and contentment wash over you as you connect with the natural world around you.

Step 4: Relaxation

Find a comfortable spot to sit by the water's edge, allowing yourself to relax fully. Close your eyes and take a few more deep breaths, sensing the peacefulness of your surroundings. With each inhale, imagine yourself relaxing. With each exhale, imagine releasing any remaining tension or worry from your body and mind.

Step 5: Reflecting on Inner Peace

Take a moment to reflect on how you feel in this peaceful place. Notice any sensations of relaxation or inner harmony that arise inside you. Allow yourself to relax in these feelings of gratitude for the present moment. Remind yourself that you can return to this place of inner peace whenever you need to find a moment of calm in your day.

Step 6: Returning to the Present

When you feel ready, slowly begin to bring your subconscious back to the room around you. Stretch your muscles, and gently wiggle you toes and fingers. Carry the feelings of peace and tranquility with you as you continue with your day.

After you have completed this visual exercise, think about the stress and negative emotions you feel on a daily basis and allow yourself to reflect on them.

_____

_____

_____

_____

How do you feel about these emotions and feelings after completing the visualization?

_____

_____

_____

_____

Do you feel like this exercise helped at all? If you answered no, take some time to consider why and how you can make improvements.

_____

_____

_____

_____

_____

Expressive Art Therapy Worksheet

The expressive art therapy activity worksheet is designed to help you explore your thoughts, feelings, and experiences through the creative process of art-making.

Step 1: Preparation

Gather your art supplies, such as paper, markers, crayons, paints, or any other materials you enjoy working with. Find a quiet space where you can engage in the creative process without distractions. Take a few moments to center yourself and set an intention for your art-making process. Consider what you would like to explore or express through your artwork.

Step 2: Setting the Mood

Create a calming atmosphere. Light a candle or play music to enhance your sense of relaxation and creativity. Allow yourself to let go of any expectations or judgments about your artistic skills and focus on the process of creation.

Step 3: Exploration

Begin by selecting a color, shape, or image that resonates with your emotions. Use this as a starting point for your artwork, and allow your insight to guide your art. Express your emotions through your art-making process. Allow yourself to experiment with different techniques and materials, and let your inner feelings flow onto the page without restriction.

Step 4: Reflection

Once you have completed your artwork, take a step back and observe it. Notice any thoughts, feelings, or memories that arise as you view the art. Reflect on the meaning behind your artwork.

What did you draw?

_____

_____

_____

_____

How does it make you feel?

_____

_____

_____

_____

What materials and colors did you choose?

_____

_____

_____

_____

Why did you choose these materials?

_____

_____

_____

_____

What emotions or experiences does it represent for you?

_____

_____

_____

_____

How does it make you feel to see your thoughts and feelings expressed visually?

_____

_____

_____

_____

If drawing isn't something you enjoy, explore other creative activities that resonate with you, such as journaling, collage-making, or sculpture.

Somatic Movement Therapy – A Reconnection with your Body's Natural Rhythms

Somatic movement therapy is a form of therapy that combines somatic therapy with movement therapy or exercises, such as dance, yoga, etc. It emphasizes internal movement over external motion, focusing on the sensations within the body rather than outward actions.

Internal movement differs significantly from conventional physical exercise routines. By cultivating this internal awareness, known as interoception, people can experience an increased sense of well-being.

As individuals master somatic movement techniques, they often find themselves making more informed choices regarding their overall health and wellness.

So, what exactly is somatic movement? Somatic Movement Therapy provides individuals with the tools necessary to tap into the body's inherent wisdom. By addressing and releasing tension patterns that contribute to pain and restrictions, somatic movement therapy promotes physical comfort and enhanced mobility. These patterns may stem from various factors, such as physical injuries or trauma.

Engaging in gentle movement can bring reflective changes in both the body and mind. Research from the Laban Institute illustrates how increased sensory awareness positively impacts posture, mood elevation, and emotional expression. Similarly, studies conducted by the HM Alexander Center shed light on the efficacy of internally focused movement in easing symptoms associated with Parkinson's disease.

While further research is needed, existing research suggests that fostering a deeper mind-body connection through movement leads to improved well-being, increased flexibility, and enhanced adaptability in navigating life's challenges.

Somatic movement promotes the brain's capacity to reorganize and adapt by forming new patterns and habits. This translates to improved muscle control, balance perception, stress response, and emotional regulation. For individuals experiencing chronic pain, the ability to rewire neural pathways offers a way to change their perception of the world around them.

Somatic movement serves as a vital factor in strengthening the body-mind connection. When individuals feel disconnected from their bodies, they may experience feelings of disorientation, anxiety, or depression. Mental hyperactivity often manifests in physical discomforts such as digestive issues, muscle tension, or headaches.

Somatic movement therapy provides the tools to reestablish this connection. They become better equipped to navigate challenges, manage stress, and find comfort in their bodies. As movement refines and the brain adapts, individuals discover a newfound ease in inhabiting their bodies, making thoughts and emotions more manageable.

Yoga

Yoga, when paired with somatic therapy, offers a powerful combination of movement-based therapy. Both practices focus on connecting the mind and body through mindful movement and breath awareness. In yoga, various poses are practiced to promote flexibility, strength, and relaxation. Somatic therapy, on the other hand, emphasizes internal sensations and body awareness to release tension and trauma stored in the body.

By incorporating yoga into somatic therapy sessions, individuals can deepen their understanding of their body's sensations and movement patterns. Yoga can help individuals tune into their bodies, identify areas of tension, and explore new ways of moving. For example, practicing gentle yoga poses can promote relaxation and ease tension in muscles, while more dynamic poses can build strength and mobility.

Additionally, breath awareness refined in yoga can complement somatic therapy techniques by helping individuals regulate their nervous system and manage stress. By focusing on the breath during yoga practice, people can learn to keep the mind calm, reduce anxiety, and increase overall awareness of bodily sensations.

Furthermore, yoga provides a safe environment for individuals to explore their bodies and emotions. In a somatic therapy session that incorporates yoga, individuals may be encouraged to explore how specific yoga poses or movements evoke different emotions or sensations. This exploration can help people deeply understand the mind-body connection and how it influences their overall well-being.

Moreover, the philosophy of yoga, which emphasizes self-acceptance, compassion, and non-judgment, aligns closely with the principles of somatic therapy. Through yoga practice, individuals can cultivate greater self-awareness, self-compassion, and acceptance of themselves and their experiences.

Another benefit of pairing yoga with somatic therapy is its potential for increased body awareness and emotional regulation. As individuals become more attuned to their body's sensations and responses during yoga practice, they may develop greater resilience and coping skills for managing difficult emotions or experiences outside of the yoga practice.

Overall, yoga and somatic therapy can complement each other beautifully as movement-based therapies. Together, they offer individuals a holistic approach to healing that joins the mind, body, and spirit. Through regular practice, individuals can experience increased relaxation, improved body awareness, and enhanced emotional well-being.

Wall Pilates

Pairing Wall Pilates with somatic therapy can offer individuals a unique and effective approach to movement-based therapy. Wall Pilates, a variation of traditional Pilates exercises performed using a wall for support, focuses on improving strength, flexibility, and alignment while also promoting body awareness and mindfulness. Somatic therapy, on the other hand, emphasizes the connection between the mind and body to release tension and trauma stored in the body.

By integrating Wall Pilates into somatic therapy sessions, individuals can enhance their body awareness and deepen their understanding of movement patterns. Wall Pilates exercises, which utilize the support of the wall for stability, can help individuals explore their range of motion, identify areas of tension, and improve posture and alignment.

Furthermore, the emphasis on breath control and mindfulness in Wall Pilates aligns with the principles of somatic therapy. Participants can learn to regulate their nervous systems, reduce stress, and increase overall awareness of bodily sensations.

Moreover, Wall Pilates provides a safe and supportive environment for people to explore their bodies and movement capabilities. In a somatic therapy session that incorporates Wall Pilates, individuals may be encouraged to explore how specific exercises or movements affect their bodies and emotions. This exploration can help individuals develop a deeper understanding of the mind-body connection and its impact on their overall well-being.

Additionally, Wall Pilates can help individuals build strength and stability, which are essential components of somatic therapy. Strengthening the body through Wall Pilates exercises can provide individuals with a sense of empowerment and resilience, allowing them to better cope with stress and trauma.

Furthermore, the use of props and modifications in Wall Pilates allows for personalized and accessible movement experiences, making it suitable for individuals of all fitness levels and abilities. In a somatic therapy session, the adaptability of Wall Pilates exercises can be personalized to meet the unique needs and goals of each individual.

Overall, pairing Wall Pilates with somatic therapy offers individuals a comprehensive approach to movement-based therapy that integrates physical, emotional, and psychological aspects of healing. Through regular practice, individuals can experience increased strength, flexibility, body awareness, and emotional well-being, ultimately leading to a greater sense of empowerment and vitality.

Body Expressions Collage Worksheet

This body expressions collage activity worksheet will help you explore and celebrate your unique identity and experiences through the creation of a collage.

Step 1: Preparation

Gather your collage collage materials. These can include materials such as photos, sciddors, newspapers, fabric scraps, magazines, glue, and markers etc. Take a moment to consider what aspects of yourself you would like to express through your artwork.

Step 2: Setting the Mood

Create a calming environment for collage-making activities. Play your favorite music, light a candle, or surround yourself with images or objects that resonate with your mood. Take a few deep breaths to ground yourself. Allow yourself to let go of any self-doubt or judgment and accept the creative flow and process.

Step 3: Exploring Body Expression

Begin the activity by selecting images, words, or symbols from your collage materials that represent different aspects of your body, identity, and experiences. Look for images that evoke emotions and memories for you. Arrange the images on your collage surface, allowing your artistic sense to guide your creative expression. Experiment with different combinations until you find a layout that feels true to you.

Step 4: Reflection

Once you have completed your collage, take a step back and observe it. Notice the colors, shapes, and textures that emerge from your arrangement of images and materials. Reflect on the meaning behind your collage.

Why did you choose these images and materials?

_____

_____

_____

_____

What aspects of yourself are you expressing through this collage?

_____

_____

_____

_____

How do the images and words you've chosen reflect your identity and experiences?

_____

_____

_____

_____

_____

Step 5: Embrace Your True Self

Acknowledge any insights or discoveries you have gained from this creative process. Remember that your body expression collage is a reflection of your true self.

Creative Expression Integration Worksheet

This activity is designed to help you integrate insights and discoveries from your creative expressions into your daily life.

Step 1: Preparation

Gather any creative expressions you've completed, such as artwork, writing, or other forms of self-expression. Find a quiet and comfortable space where you can reflect without distractions. Centre yourself and set an intention for this integration process. Consider what learning you hope to carry forward from your creative expressions.

Step 2: Setting the Mood

Create a peaceful atmosphere for your integration process. Light a candle, play music, and practice deep breathing or meditation. Allow yourself to relax and be present in the moment. Let go of any expectations or judgments about what you should or shouldn't feel during this process.

Step 3: Reflecting on Creative Expressions

Begin by revisiting your creative expressions one by one. Observe them with fresh eyes and an open mind, and allow yourself to fully experience the emotions and thoughts they bring. Notice any themes, patterns, or repeating symbols that occur across your creative expressions. Pay attention to the feelings and sensations they evoke inside you. Write these down in detail.

_____

_____

_____

_____

Step 4: Integrating Insights

Reflect on the insights you have gained from your creative expressions. Consider how they relate to your life experiences, beliefs, and aspirations. Write them down.

_____

_____

_____

_____

Identify any steps or changes you can make in your daily life based on these insights.

_____

_____

_____

_____

_____

How can you apply the wisdom and lessons learned from your creative expressions to promote harmony and fulfillment?

_____

_____

_____

_____

Step 5: Create Balance

The next step in this exercise is to explore ways to incorporate creativity and self-expression into your daily routine. Consider activities such as journaling, mindfulness practices, or engaging in creative hobbies. Find a balance between introspection and action, and allow yourself to both reflect on your inner experiences and engage with the world around you.

Safe Space – A Supportive Environment for Growth and Healing

Creating a healing and welcoming environment in somatic therapy is essential for developing growth and recovery in patients. Somatic therapy focuses on the mind-body connection, helping individuals release stored tension and trauma through mindful movement and awareness. By ensuring the environment is safe, supportive, and nurturing, patients can fully engage in the therapeutic process and experience meaningful transformation.

A healing environment in somatic therapy begins with a comfortable and calm physical space. This includes a quiet room, a comfortable setting, and minimal distractions. Such an environment helps patients feel at ease and ready to focus on their inner experiences. The space should be adaptable, allowing for various therapeutic activities such as gentle movement, breathing exercises, and body awareness practices.

In addition to the physical setting, an individual's attitude plays a crucial role in creating a welcoming atmosphere. A compassionate and non-judgmental approach is vital, as it motivates you to think about your experiences and emotions openly. Always actively listen, validate your feelings, and welcome gentle guidance throughout the exercises. Building a sense of trust and rapport with yourself is essential for creating a sense of safety and security.

In somatic therapy, the incorporation of mindful movement practices like Yoga and Wall Pilates can enhance the healing experience and emotional growth. These practices encourage you to connect with your body, explore your feelings, and release physical and emotional tension. Yoga offers a range of poses and sequences that promote relaxation, flexibility, and strength, while Wall Pilates provides support and stability, helping you to improve your posture and alignment. Both practices emphasize breath awareness, which aids in regulating the nervous system and reducing stress.

The integration of these movement practices within somatic therapy sessions allows you to develop greater body awareness and mindfulness. As you engage in these activities, you will learn to recognize areas of tension, understand your movement patterns, and explore new ways of moving. This process helps you to release stored trauma and develop healthier, more adaptive responses to stress and emotional challenges.

Creating a healing and welcoming environment also involves respecting your unique journey. Encouraging self-compassion and self-acceptance is crucial, as it will help you to embrace your experiences and move forward with greater resilience and confidence.

Overall, a healing and welcoming environment in somatic therapy is characterized by a supportive physical space, a compassionate approach, and the integration of mindful movement practices. This holistic approach nurtures a deep sense of safety, allowing you to explore your inner world, release tension, and experience profound growth and healing. Through regular engagement in somatic therapy, you can achieve greater well-being, emotional balance, and a stronger connection between mind and body.

A Grounding Mindset – Setting the Stage for Somatic Exploration

Before engaging in somatic exercises, it is crucial to develop a grounding mindset. This preparation involves becoming mentally and emotionally focused, which provides a firm foundation for exploring and understanding the body's sensations and movements. Grounding techniques can include mindfulness exercises, such as focusing on the breath or visualizing roots spreading from the feet into the earth; this helps individuals feel attached and present.

A grounding mindset promotes a state of stability and calmness. This helps lessen the effects of stress and anxiety, creating an inner environment where you will feel safe and secure. When the mind is preoccupied with worries, it becomes challenging to recognize the indirect signals that the body sends. By practicing grounding, you can become more familiar with your internal experiences.

Setting the stage for somatic exploration involves more than just mental preparation; it also includes creating a helpful physical environment. This might mean finding a quiet, comfortable space free from distractions where you can focus on the sensations inside the body. Wearing comfortable clothing that allows one to perform free movement can also enhance the experience, making it easier to notice and respond to bodily signals.

As you become more grounded, you can more effectively engage in somatic practices. These practices often require a high level of body awareness and the ability to stay present with one's physical self and emotional experiences. A grounded mindset supports this by providing a stable stage to explore. It allows you to observe your body sensations without judgment, fostering a deeper connection between mind and body.

The benefits of this approach are noteworthy. Enhanced self-awareness allows you to recognize patterns of tension and stress within your body, which can be recognized and released. Emotional regulation improves as you learn to identify and process your feelings through your body sensations. Overall well-being is promoted as the integration of mind and body leads to a more harmonious and balanced state of mind.

So, developing a grounding mindset before engaging in somatic practices is essential for maximizing the benefits of these activities. By becoming mentally and emotionally focused, you can create a stable foundation for deeper somatic exploration. This preparation enhances self-awareness, supports emotional regulation, and contributes to overall well-being, making somatic exercises and practices a more effective and transformative experience.

The following somatic exercises, supplemented by yoga and Wall Pilates, present a holistic approach to health in just 10 minutes. Each exercise, which lasts 10 minutes, helps alleviate stress and trauma all over the body while also providing relief for issues such as chronic pain, anxiety, digestive health, etc.

Chapter 1: Somatic Exercises for Stress Relief and Anxiety Management

Somatic exercises are powerful practices that can significantly aid in stress relief and anxiety management. These movement therapies focus on the mind-body connection, allowing you to release pent-up tension and promote a sense of calm. One key feature of these practices is their ability to help balance hormones, which play a vital role in maintaining mood and stress levels.

When practicing somatic yoga, gentle movements and mindful breathing techniques activate the parasympathetic nervous system. This helps reduce cortisol levels, the hormone related to stress. Lower cortisol levels lead to a calmer state of mind and reduced feelings of anxiety. The stretching and holding of poses in somatic yoga also improve blood circulation, which can further enhance mood and energy levels.

These exercises not only strengthen the body with their range of movements but also promote relaxation by releasing tension stored in the muscles. The focus on controlled breathing during Pilates exercises aids in oxygenating the body and calming the nervous system. This practice can also stimulate the production of endorphins, these are natural mood booster hormones that the bod produces, leading to a sense of happiness and reduced anxiety. By paying attention to physical sensations and breathing, you can interrupt the cycle of negative thoughts and bring your focus back to the present moment. This mindfulness helps in recognizing and releasing physical displays of stress, such as muscle tightness and shallow breathing.

In addition to hormonal balance, these practices positively affect various body parts, including the vagus nerve, which plays a key role in the parasympathetic nervous system. Activating the vagus nerve through deep, mindful breathing can reduce heart rate and blood pressure, creating a state of relaxation. The given exercises can help you become less stressed and anxious.

Legs-Up-the-Wall Pose

Instructions:

1. Find a clear wall space with enough area to comfortably perform this exercise.

2. Start by lying down on the ground. Swing one leg up along the wall while keeping the other leg bent on the ground in a comfortable position.

3. Position yourself so that your hips are comfortably near the wall.

4. Relax your arms on your stomach or by your sides in a relaxed position.

5. Focus on your breath while keeping your eyes closed, hold this position for at least 3-4 minutes.

6. Afterwards, switch the position of your legs and continue to breathe mindfully for 3-4 minutes.

7. Now, gently bend your knees and roll to one side, coming out of the pose.

8. Take a moment to rest, staying in the same position before sitting up.

Additional Benefits:

- Reduces stress and anxiety
- Enhances blood circulation
- Relieves tired or swollen legs
- Gently stretches the back, legs, and neck

Child's Pose

Instructions:

1. For this pose, make sure to use a soft yoga mat, as the majority of your body weight will rest on your knees, which may cause discomfort.

2. Start the pose by sitting on your knees on the ground or on a soft mat.

3. Now, spread your knees apart. This space should be enough to comfortably fit your torso in between your thighs.

4. Rest your hips on your heels, spread your arms outwards, and place your palms flat on the floor.

5. Lower your chest towards the floor, and rest your forehead on the mat. Hold for at least 3-4 minutes.

6. Now, bring your arms alongside your body with your palms facing up, and hold for at least 3-4 minutes.

7. Allow your body to relax into the pose, breathing deeply and letting go of tension with each exhale.

Additional Benefits:

- Gently stretches hips, thighs, and ankles
- Reduces stress and fatigue
- Promotes grounding and relaxation
- Alleviates back and neck pain

Corpse Pose

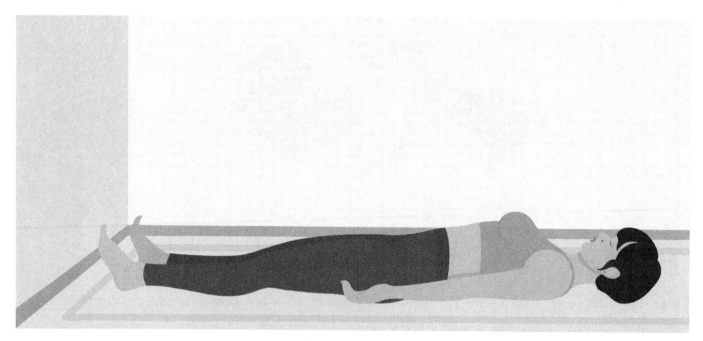

Instructions:

1. Lie down on your back on a soft yoga mat.

2. Your feet should fall open, with your toes pointing outwards.

3. Rest your arms alongside your body, palms facing up, and fingers naturally curled.

4. Close your eyes and relax your body, from your toes to your head.

5. Relax your facial muscles, jaw, and forehead, and let your breath flow naturally.

6. Allow your body to sink into the floor, releasing any tension with each exhale.

7. Stay in this pose for several minutes, fully relax and let go.

Additional Benefits:

- Calms the nervous system

- Promotes deep rest and relaxation

- Improves mental clarity and concentration

Worksheet

Reader Check-In! Now that you've gone through a few exercises, stop for a few minutes to breathe and check-in!

Answer the following questions to get a better understanding of how your body works with the exercises in this section!

Name: _____   Date: _____

1. **Experience:**

   • Excellent

   • Good

   • Fair

   • Poor

2. **Instructions:**

   • Excellent

   • Good

   • Fair

   • Poor

3. **Structure:**

   • Was the pace suitable for your experience?

     ○ Yes

     ○ It was complicated

     ○ It was too simplified

4. Exercise and Difficulty:

- How challenging did you find the yoga poses?

    - ○ Very challenging

    - ○ Mildly challenging

    - ○ Just right

    - ○ Not challenging enough

5. Personal Impact:

- How do you feel physically after the session?

    - ○ Energized and refreshed

    - ○ Relaxed and calm

    - ○ No significant change

    - ○ Tired or sore

- How do you feel mentally and emotionally after the session?

    - ○ Balanced and peaceful

    - ○ Positive and uplifted

    - ○ No significant change

    - ○ Stressed or anxious

Did these exercises help you lessen your stress and pain?

_____

_____

_____

Do you see yourself continuing these practices in the future? Why or why not?

_____

_____

_____

Wall Roll Down

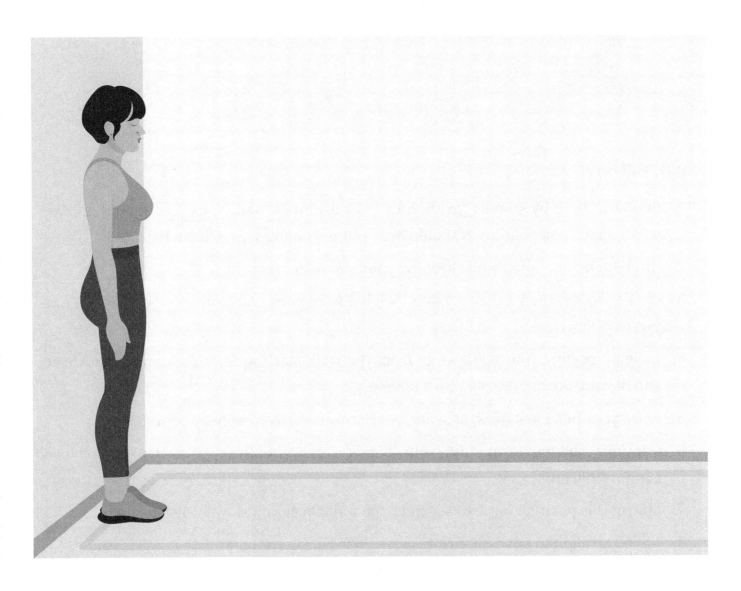

Instructions:

1. Start the pose by standing with your back against a wall. Your feet should be hip-width apart, and your heels should be about 6-12 inches away from the wall.

2. Straighten your spine while keeping your shoulders relaxed.

3. Inhale slowly, then exhale as you slowly lower your chin towards your chest, one vertebra at a time.

4. Imagine peeling your spine away from the wall, starting from the top of your head and moving down towards your tailbone.

5. Relax your head and neck, allowing your arms to hang loosely by your side.

6. Continue rolling down until your hands reach the floor or as far as you can comfortably go.

7. Stay in this position for 5-10 seconds, then inhale as you slowly roll back up.

8. As you straighten yourself, firmly press your back into the wall.

9. Repeat this exercise for at least 8-10 minutes.

Additional Benefits:

- Stretches spine and hamstrings

- Improves posture and alignment

- Relieves back and neck tension

- Enhances body awareness and flexibility

Wall Angel

Instructions:

1. Start the exercise by standing with your back against a wall. Your feet should be hip-width apart, and your heels about 6-12 inches away from the wall.

2. Keep your upper body, head and buttocks in contact with the wall.

3. Raise your arms above you, bending them at the elbows.

4. Bend you arms at the elbows upwards, and press them against the wall. Make sure that your elbows and wrists are in contact with the wall.

5. Flatten your lower back against the wall and inhale deeply.

6. Now, exhale as you slide your arms up the wall, keeping your elbows and wrists in contact with the wall.

7. Continue sliding your arms up as high as you can. Your lower back should stay in contact with the wall as you do so.

8. Once your arms are as high as you can comfortably go, pause and hold for at least 5 seconds.

9. Now, inhale and slowly slide your arms back down the wall, returning to the starting pose.

10. Repeat the movement at least 8-10 minutes.

Additional Benefits:

- Improves shoulder mobility and posture

- Opens up the chest

- Strengthens upper back muscles

- Corrects imbalances and helps with spine alignment

- Alleviates shoulder and upper back tension

Worksheet

Reader Check-In! Now that you've gone through a few exercises, stop for a few minutes to breathe and check-in!

Answer the following questions to get a better understanding of how your body works with the exercises in this section!

Name: _____   Date: _____

1. **Experience:**

- How would you rate your overall experience with the Wall Pilates session?

   - ○ Excellent

   - ○ Good

   - ○ Fair

   - ○ Poor

2. **Instructions:**

- Rate the instructions.

   - ○ Excellent

   - ○ Good

   - ○ Fair

   - ○ Poor

3. **Structure:**

- Was the pace of the instructions appropriate for your fitness level?

   - ○ Yes

   - ○ It was complicated

   - ○ It was too simple

4. **Exercise and Difficulty:**

- How challenging did you find the exercises?

    - ○ Very challenging

    - ○ Mildly challenging

    - ○ Just right

    - ○ Not challenging enough

- Were the exercises and sequences clearly explained and demonstrated?

    - ○ Yes, very clearly

    - ○ Somewhat clearly

    - ○ Not clearly enough

5. **Personal Impact:**

- How do you feel physically after the session?

    - ○ Energized and strong

    - ○ Relaxed and balanced

    - ○ No significant change

    - ○ Tired or sore

- How do you feel mentally and emotionally after the session?

    - ○ Balanced and peaceful

    - ○ Positive and uplifted

    - ○ No significant change

    - ○ Stressed or anxious

Did these exercises help you lessen your stress and pain?

_____

_____

_____

Do you see yourself continuing these practices in the future? Why or why not?

_____

_____

_____

Chapter 2: Somatic Exercises for Weight Loss

Somatic exercises, which combine mindful movement with physical exercise, can be highly effective for weight loss. These practices focus on the mind-body connection, encouraging awareness of bodily sensations and promoting a deeper understanding of hunger and satiety cues, which can prevent overeating.

Somatic exercises involve gentle yet impactful movements that increase flexibility and muscle tone, increase metabolism, and help with weight management. The emphasis on mindful breathing and relaxation techniques helps reduce stress, which in turn lowers cortisol levels. Lower cortisol can decrease the likelihood of stress-related weight gain, like stress eating.

These exercises enhance overall strength and endurance, contributing to a higher resting metabolic rate. The practices also promote better alignment and balance, making other physical activities more effective and reducing the chance of injury. These exercises offer a holistic approach to weight loss, integrating physical activity with mindfulness to support long-term health and fitness goals.

Supine Twist

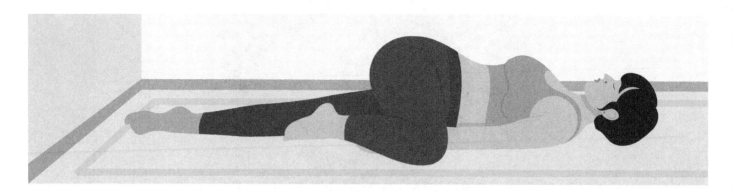

Instructions:

1. To practice this pose, lie down comfortably on a yoga mat.

2. Spread your arms out to the sides in a "T" shape, with your palms facing down.

3. Bend your right leg at the knee and bring it closer to your chest while keeping the left leg extended straight.

4. Use your core muscles and keep your spine neutral.

5. Exhale and slowly bring your bent knee to the right side of your body, and slowly lower it to the floor.

6. Keep both shoulders touching on the mat, and turn your head towards the left side.

7. You can also place your left hand on top of your right knee to deepen the stretch.

8. Hold the twist for several minutes, feeling the stretch along your spine and outer hip.

9. Inhale, and repeat the same pose on the opposite side.

Additional Benefits:

- Stretches the spine and back muscles

- Massages the internal organs

- Improves spinal mobility

- Helps with digestion

- Releases tension in the lower back

High Lunge

Instructions:

1. Begin this pose while standing up straight. Keep your feet hip-width apart, and your arms should be relaxed at your sides.

2. Move your right foot into a lunge position by lowering it to the floor.

3. Make sure that your left knee is aligned above your left ankle, creating a 90-degree angle with your left leg.

4. Keep your right leg extended behind you; the top of your foot should rest on the mat.

5. Take a slow, deep breath and lift your arms towards the ceiling.

6. Slowly move your hips down towards the mat.

7. Tilt your head slightly back to look up between your hands.

8. Hold the pose for several minutes; your body should move deeper into the stretch with each exhale.

9. Hold for at least 4-5 minutes and repeat the pose on the opposite side.

Additional Benefits:

- Strengthens legs and glutes

- Stretches hips and groin

- Improves balance and stability

- Enhances core strength

- Increases flexibility in the legs

Downward-Facing Dog

Instructions:

1. Start this pose on your hands and feet in a push-up position.

2. Spread your fingers apart and press firmly into the mat with your palms; this will create a strong foundation for the pose.

3. Now lift your hips towards the ceiling, and straighten your arms and legs to form an V shape with your body.

4. Your hands should be shoulder-width apart and your feet hip-width apart.

5. Push your chest towards your thighs; this process will help lengthen your spine and create space between your vertebrae.

6. Let your head hang freely between your arms.

7. Press your heels down on the mat as much as you comfortably can.

8. If you feel any strain in your lower back, bend your knees slightly to ease the pressure.

9. Hold the pose for several minutes, focusing on straightening your spine and relaxing your neck and shoulders.

Additional Benefits:

- Provides a deep stretch to the hamstrings, calves and shoulders
- Develops the arms and leg muscles
- Relieves tension in the spine
- Improves body flexibility
- Enhances circulation and energizes the body

Worksheet

Reader Check-In! Now that you've gone through a few exercises, stop for a few minutes to breathe and check-in!

Answer the following questions to get a better understanding of how your body works with the exercises in this section!

Name: _____   Date: _____

1. **Experience:**

   - Excellent

   - Good

   - Fair

   - Poor

2. **Instructions:**

   - Excellent

   - Good

   - Fair

   - Poor

3. **Structure:**

   - Was the pace suitable for your experience?

     ○ Yes

     ○ It was complicated

     ○ It was too simplified

4. **Exercise and Difficulty:**

* How challenging did you find the yoga poses?

  - ○ Very challenging

  - ○ Mildly challenging

  - ○ Just right

  - ○ Not challenging enough

5. **Personal Impact:**

* How do you feel physically after the session?

  - ○ Energized and refreshed

  - ○ Relaxed and calm

  - ○ No significant change

  - ○ Tired or sore

* How do you feel mentally and emotionally after the session?

  - ○ Balanced and peaceful

  - ○ Positive and uplifted

  - ○ No significant change

  - ○ Stressed or anxious

Did these exercises help you lessen your stress and pain?

_____

_____

_____

Do you see yourself continuing these practices in the future? Why or why not?

_____

_____

_____

Wall Squat

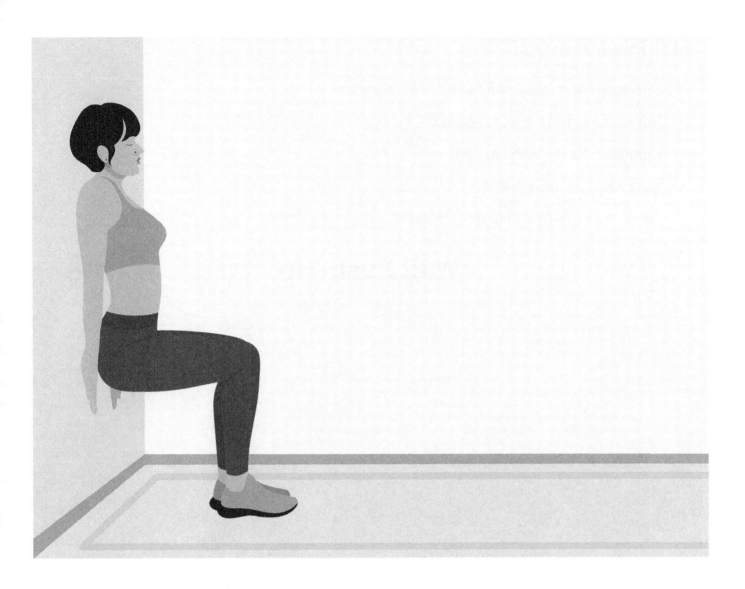

Instructions:

1. Start this pose with your back against a wall keeping your feet hip-width apart, and heels about 6-12 inches away from the wall.

2. Take a deep breath, and then exhale as you slowly lower your body into a squat and slide your back down the wall.

3. Keep your knees aligned with your ankles.

4. Lower your body until your thighs are as far down as you can comfortably go.

5. Press your back into the wall, and keep your chest lifted.

6. Hold the squat position for 3-5 seconds. Then, gradually come out of this position, and maintain deep breathing.

7. Repeat this movement for at least 8-10 minutes.

Additional Benefits:

- Strengthens quads, hamstrings, and glutes

- Improves endurance and stamina

- Enhances lower body stability

- Engages core muscles

- Supports knee health and function

Wall Push-Up

Instructions:

1. Start the pose by standing and facing a wall, keeping your feet hip-width apart and your arms extended in front of you. Your palms should be flat against the wall, shoulder-width apart.

2. Take a few steps back, keeping your palms and upper body close to the wall. This will create a small angle between yourself and the wall. The further you step back, the more difficult the exercise will become.

3. Inhale, then exhale and bend your elbows. Bring your chest towards the wall, keeping your body in a straight line.

4. Lower your chest until it nearly touches the wall or as far down as you can comfortably go.

5. Inhale, push your palms against the wall and return to the starting position.

6. Repeat this exercise for at least 8-10 minutes.

7. If this exercise feels too challenging, you can adjust the angle by stepping closer to the wall.

Additional Benefits:

- Strengthens chest, shoulders, and arms
- Enhances upper body stamina
- Improves posture
- Engages core muscles
- Provides an alternative to push-ups

Worksheet

Reader Check-In! Now that you've gone through a few exercises, stop for a few minutes to breathe and check-in!

Answer the following questions to get a better understanding of how your body works with the exercises in this section!

Name: _____   Date: _____

1. **Experience:**

- How would you rate your overall experience with the Wall Pilates session?

    ○ Excellent

    ○ Good

    ○ Fair

    ○ Poor

2. **Instructions:**

- How would you rate the instructions?

    ○ Excellent

    ○ Good

    ○ Fair

    ○ Poor

3. **Structure:**

- Was the pace of the instructions appropriate for your fitness level?

    ○ Yes

    ○ It was complicated

    ○ It was too simple

4. Exercise and Difficulty:

- How challenging did you find the exercises?

  - ○ Very challenging
  - ○ Mildly challenging
  - ○ Just right
  - ○ Not challenging enough

- Were the exercises and sequences clearly explained and demonstrated?

  - ○ Yes, very clearly
  - ○ Somewhat clearly
  - ○ Not clearly enough

5. Personal Impact:

- How do you feel physically after the session?

  - ○ Energized and strong
  - ○ Relaxed and balanced
  - ○ No significant change
  - ○ Tired or sore

- How do you feel mentally and emotionally after the session?

  - ○ Balanced and peaceful
  - ○ Positive and uplifted
  - ○ No significant change
  - ○ Stressed or anxious

Did these exercises help you lessen your stress and pain?

_____

_____

_____

Do you see yourself continuing these practices in the future? Why or why not?

_____

_____

_____

Chapter 3: Somatic Exercises for Chronic Pain Alleviation

Somatic exercises can be influential in alleviating chronic pain by promoting body awareness and mindful movement. The practices in this section focus on gentle, controlled exercises that help release tension and improve overall body alignment, addressing the root causes of chronic discomfort.

Somatic exercises, on the whole, employ deliberate movements combined with deep breathing, which helps in reducing muscle tension and increasing flexibility. This approach enhances blood circulation and promotes the access of oxygen and nutrients to the body, which can speed up healing and reduce pain. The mindful aspect of these exercises helps you become more aware of your body's needs, allowing you to adjust movements to avoid pain and prevent injury. Somatic exercises enable you to perform exercises that strengthen core muscles and improve posture without overstraining. These exercises target deep muscle groups, helping to stabilize and support the spine and joints. Improved posture and muscle strength can alleviate pressure on nerves and reduce pain, mainly in the back, neck, and shoulders.

Somatic exercises help break the cycle of pain and tension by fostering a state of mental calm and physical ease, providing long-term relief and enhancing overall well-being.

Seated Forward Bend

Instructions:

1. Begin this pose on the floor. Your legs should be spread straight in front of you.

2. Keep your spine straight and your feet flexed. Your toes should point towards the ceiling.

3. Now, inhale and reach your arms towards the ceiling.

4. Then, exhale and bend forward, bringing your chest to your knees.

5. Bring your arms to grab onto your shins, ankles, or feet, depending on your flexibility.

6. You can also use a strap or towel looped around your feet to help lengthen your reach.

7. Keep your neck relaxed and keep your eyes on your legs.

8. Hold the pose for several minutes, and feel the stretch along the back of your legs and spine.

Additional Benefits:

- Stretches the spine, hamstrings, and lower back
- Calms the mind and reduces stress
- Improves digestion
- Enhances flexibility in the legs and back
- Relieves tension in the lower back

Supine Bound Angle Pose

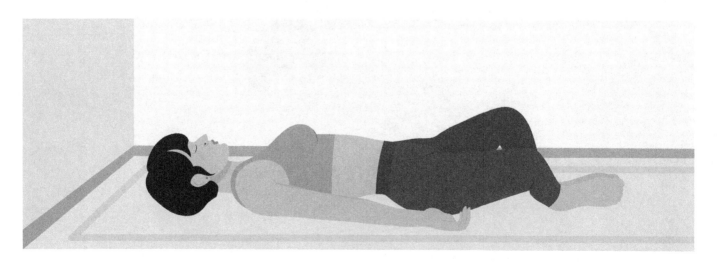

Instructions:

1. Begin the pose on your back on a yoga mat.

2. Bend your knees and join the soles of your feet together; your knees will naturally fall to the sides in this pose.

3. Bring your heels close to your pelvis; your knees should touch the ground or come as close as comfortable.

4. Place your hands on your stomach or by your sides; the palms should be facing up.

5. Close your eyes and take deep breaths, and try to relax your body.

6. Stay in the pose for at least 8-10 minutes, allow your hips to open and release tension.

Additional Benefits:

- Opens the hips and groin
- Promotes relaxation and stress relief
- Stretches inner thighs and knees
- Improves circulation
- Supports relaxation and better sleep

Cobra Pose

Instructions:

1. Start the pose by lying on your stomach on a yoga mat.

2. Place your palms on the yoga mat next to your ribs; your elbows should bend and tuck close to your sides.

3. Press the tops of your feet and thighs into the mat.

4. Inhale, and lift your head and chest off the ground.

5. Keep your eyes looking slightly upwards.

6. Put weight your palms into the mat to lift your chest a little higher.

7. Stay in this position for at least 5-8 minutes. If you're comfortable, lift your chest higher by strengthening your arms.

8. Hold the pose for several breaths while breathing deeply, and focus on broadening your chest with each inhale.

Additional Benefits:

- Strengthens the spine and lower back muscles
- Opens the chest and shoulders
- Improves spine flexibility
- Enhances respiratory function
- Reduces stress and fatigue

Worksheet

Reader Check-In! Now that you've gone through a few exercises, stop for a few minutes to breathe and check-in!

Answer the following questions to get a better understanding of how your body works with the exercises in this section!

Name: _____   Date: _____

1. **Experience:**

   - Excellent

   - Good

   - Fair

   - Poor

2. **Instructions:**

   - Excellent

   - Good

   - Fair

   - Poor

3. **Structure:**

   - Was the pace suitable for your experience?

     ○ Yes

     ○ It was complicated

     ○ It was too simplified

4. **Exercise and Difficulty:**

- How challenging did you find the yoga poses?

    - ○ Very challenging
    - ○ Mildly challenging
    - ○ Just right
    - ○ Not challenging enough

5. **Personal Impact:**

- How do you feel physically after the session?

    - ○ Energized and refreshed
    - ○ Relaxed and calm
    - ○ No significant change
    - ○ Tired or sore

- How do you feel mentally and emotionally after the session?

    - ○ Balanced and peaceful
    - ○ Positive and uplifted
    - ○ No significant change
    - ○ Stressed or anxious

Did these exercises help you lessen your stress and pain?

_____

_____

_____

Do you see yourself continuing these practices in the future? Why or why not?

_____

_____

_____

Wall Leg Slide

Instructions:

1. Lie down on the floor with your hips close to a wall.

2. Extend your legs straight up against the wall; your heels should be pressing into the wall.

3. Press your lower back into the floor to stabilize your pelvis.

4. Take a deep breath, then exhale and slide one or both legs down the wall, keeping them straight and lowering them towards the floor as far as you can comfortably go.

5. If you're performing this exercise one leg at a time, then keep your other leg pressing firmly into the wall.

6. Then, inhale as you slowly slide your leg back up the wall to return to the starting position.

7. Repeat this exercise for at least 8-10 minutes.

Additional Benefits:

- Strengthens thigh muscles

- Enhances hip mobility

- Improves lower body coordination

- Supports knee health

- Engages core muscles for stability

Wall Roll-Up

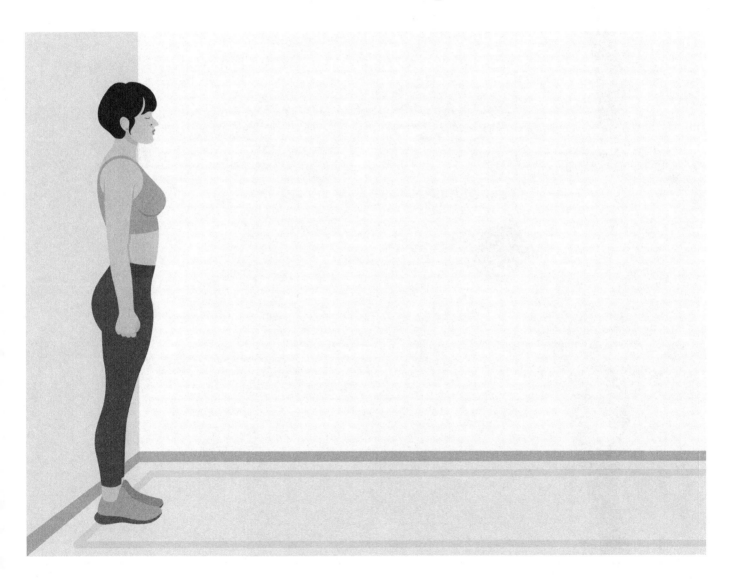

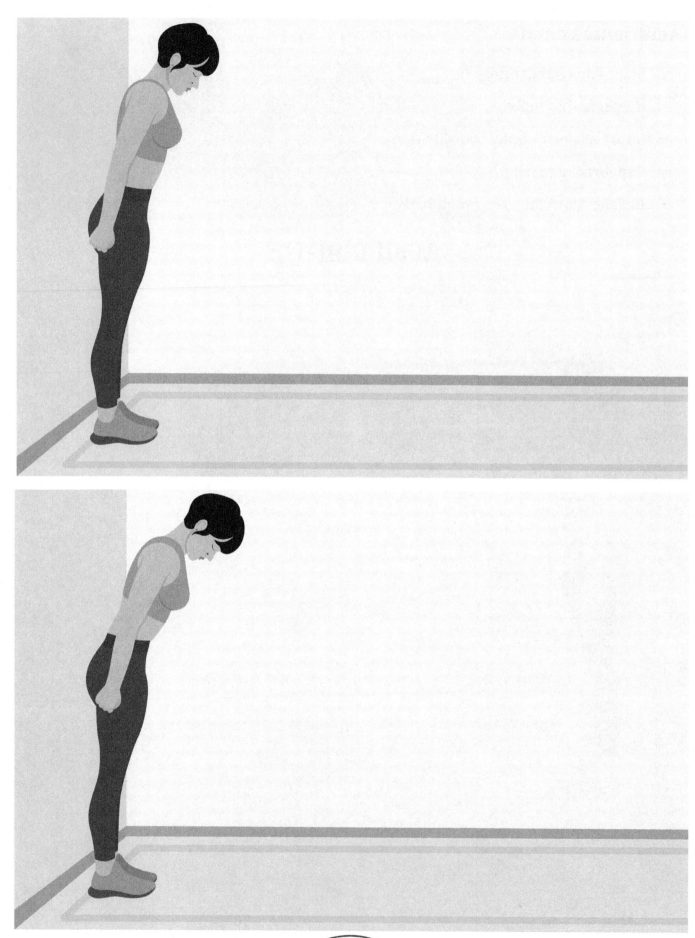

Instructions:

1. Stand on the floor with your back against a wall.

2. Place your hands on the wall next to your hips, fingers pointing towards your feet.

3. Brace your core muscles muscles to stabilize your spine and pelvis.

4. Inhale to prepare.

5. Exhale as you slowly roll your spine down towards the floor, one vertebra at a time.

6. Keep your feet flat on the floor as you lower your torso towards the ground, maintaining control throughout the movement.

7. Once your back is bent towards the floor, pause for a moment in this position.

8. Inhale as you slowly roll your spine back up the wall, one vertebra at a time.

9. Keep your feet firmly pressed to the floor and engage your core to lift your torso back up to the starting position.

10. Continue rolling up and down the wall for several minutes, moving with control and focusing on proper spinal alignment.

11. Keep your movements slow, and avoid using momentum to lift or lower your torso.

12. If you find it challenging to keep your feet flat on the floor, you can bend your knees slightly or place a small rolled-up towel under your lower back for support.

Additional Benefits:

- Stretches the spine and hamstrings
- Improves posture and spine alignment
- Relieves tension in the back and neck
- Enhances flexibility and mobility
- Engages core muscles for stability and strength

Worksheet

Reader Check-In! Now that you've gone through a few exercises, stop for a few minutes to breathe and check-in!

Answer the following questions to get a better understanding of how your body works with the exercises in this section!

Name: _____   Date: _____

1. **Experience:**

- How would you rate your overall experience with the Wall Pilates session?

   - ○ Excellent

   - ○ Good

   - ○ Fair

   - ○ Poor

2. **Instructions:**

- Rate the instructions.

   - ○ Excellent

   - ○ Good

   - ○ Fair

   - ○ Poor

3. **Structure:**

- Was the pace of the instructions appropriate for your fitness level?

   - ○ Yes

   - ○ It was complicated

   - ○ It was too simple

4. Exercise and Difficulty:

- How challenging did you find the exercises?

  - ○ Very challenging
  - ○ Mildly challenging
  - ○ Just right
  - ○ Not challenging enough

- Were the exercises and sequences clearly explained and demonstrated?

  - ○ Yes, very clearly
  - ○ Somewhat clearly
  - ○ Not clearly enough

5. Personal Impact:

- How do you feel physically after the session?

  - ○ Energized and strong
  - ○ Relaxed and balanced
  - ○ No significant change
  - ○ Tired or sore

- How do you feel mentally and emotionally after the session?

  - ○ Balanced and peaceful
  - ○ Positive and uplifted
  - ○ No significant change
  - ○ Stressed or anxious

Did these exercises help you lessen your stress and pain?

_____

_____

_____

Do you see yourself continuing these practices in the future? Why or why not?

_____

_____

_____

Chapter 4: Somatic Exercises for Digestive Health

Somatic exercises can significantly improve digestive health by enhancing the mind-body connection and promoting gentle, mindful movements. These practices focus on reducing stress and increasing physical awareness, which are crucial for maintaining a healthy digestive system.

The given exercises in this section involve slow, intentional movements combined with deep breathing exercises. These techniques stimulate the parasympathetic nervous system, often called the "rest and digest" system. Activating this system helps to reduce stress hormones like cortisol, which can negatively impact digestion. Improved blood circulation from these gentle movements also helps in the efficient functioning of digestive organs, helping to ease issues like bloating and constipation.

Somatic exercises also strengthen the abdominal muscles, enhancing the function of the digestive organs and promoting better posture. This can prevent stomach issues such as acid reflux. The emphasis on breathing and mindful movement in Somatic Wall Pilates also helps massage internal organs, facilitating smoother digestion and improving nutrient absorption.

This combination helps you become more attuned to your body's signals, promoting better eating habits and reducing stress-related digestive problems. By fostering a calm and balanced state of mind, somatic yoga, and Wall Pilates create the ideal environment for digestive health.

Seated Spinal Twist

Instructions:

1. Begin this pose by sitting on the floor with your legs stretched straight in front of you.

2. Now, bend your legs at the knees and place both feet on the floor.

3. Shift your weight slightly to the right, and then bend your left knee in a way that it folds to the outside of your right thigh.

4. Your right leg should remain extended, and your right foot should be flexed.

5. Inhale, and lift your arms to the ceiling.

6. Exhale, and twist your torso to the left. Bring your left hand behind you and your right hand to your left knee.

7. Keep your spine straight as you twist. Your neck should be able to turn, and you should be able to gaze over your left shoulder.

8. Hold this pose for at least 3-5 minutes.

9. Repeat this pose on the opposite side.

Additional Benefits:

- Enhances spine flexibility and mobility
- Stretches the shoulders, hips, and neck
- Promotes better digestion
- Relieves tension in the back
- Helps cleanse internal organs

Extended Triangle Pose

Instructions:

1. Start the pose by standing on a yoga mat with your feet hip-width apart.

2. Your feet should be wide apart (approximately 3-4 feet). However, you can adjust the distance according to your comfort and flexibility.

3. Your right foot should be pointed outward at a 90 degrees angle, and your toes should point straight. Your left foot should be turned slightly inward.

4. The right heel is in line with the arch of the left foot.

5. Inhale and stretch your arms to the sides.

6. Exhale, bend at your side, and grab your right ankle or shin with your right hand. You can also use a small block, depending on your comfort and flexibility.

7. Lift your left arm towards the ceiling.

8. Turn your head towards your left hand.

9. Hold the pose for at least 3-5 minutes.

10. Repeat the pose on the opposite side.

Additional Benefits:

- Stretches and strengthens the legs, knees, and ankles
- Opens the hips, groin, hamstrings, and shoulders
- Enhances stability and balance
- Stimulates abdominal organs
- Relieves stress and improves mental focus

Boat Pose

Instructions:

1. Start the pose by sitting on the floor with legs bent at the knees and your feet flat on the ground, hip-width apart.

2. Place your hands on the floor behind your hips. Your fingers should point towards your feet. Lean back slightly and lift your feet off the ground.

3. Keep your spine straight, and slowly straighten your legs. Bring your body into a V shape.

4. Now, stretch your arms outwards. Your palms should be facing each other.

5. Focus on balancing on your hips and hold the pose for several minutes.

6. If you're new to the pose, you can support yourself by placing your hands on the back of your thighs.

Additional Benefits:

- Strengthens the core, hips, and spine
- Improves balance and stability
- Enhances concentration and mental focus
- Tones the abdomen
- Promotes better posture

Worksheet

Reader Check-In! Now that you've gone through a few exercises, stop for a few minutes to breathe and check-in!

Answer the following questions to get a better understanding of how your body works with the exercises in this section!

Name: _____   Date: _____

1. **Experience:**

   • Excellent

   • Good

   • Fair

   • Poor

2. **Instructions:**

   • Excellent

   • Good

   • Fair

   • Poor

3. **Structure:**

   • Was the pace suitable for your experience?

      ○ Yes

      ○ It was complicated

      ○ It was too simplified

4. **Exercise and Difficulty:**

- How challenging did you find the yoga poses?

  - ○ Very challenging

  - ○ Mildly challenging

  - ○ Just right

  - ○ Not challenging enough

5. **Personal Impact:**

- How do you feel physically after the session?

  - ○ Energized and refreshed

  - ○ Relaxed and calm

  - ○ No significant change

  - ○ Tired or sore

- How do you feel mentally and emotionally after the session?

  - ○ Balanced and peaceful

  - ○ Positive and uplifted

  - ○ No significant change

  - ○ Stressed or anxious

Did these exercises help you lessen your stress and pain?

_____

_____

_____

Do you see yourself continuing these practices in the future? Why or why not?

_____

_____

_____

Wall Crunches

Instructions:

1. Lie on your back on the floor on a yoga mat. Your hips should be close to a wall and your knees bent. The soles of your feet should touch the wall.

2. Lift your arms over your chest and inhale deeply.

3. Exhale, then lift your head, neck, and shoulders off the floor in a controlled crunch motion.

4. Focus on lifting your chest towards your legs; avoid pulling on your head or neck.

5. Stay in this position for 2-3 seconds. Then inhale while slowly lowering your head, neck, and shoulders back down to the floor.

6. Repeat this exercise for at least 10 minutes.

Additional Benefits:

- Targets and strengthens the abdominal muscles
- Improves core stability
- Enhances overall muscle endurance
- Supports better posture
- Reduces strain on the back

Wall Knee Tucks

Instructions:

1. Lie down on the yoga mat on the floor, your hips should be close to a wall, and your legs should be bent with your soles touching the wall.

2. Ensure that your heels rest against the wall, and place your arms by your sides.

3. Inhale deeply, then exhale as you lift your hips slightly off the ground.

4. Keep your hips slightly lifted and the soles of your feet attached to the wall. Then, pull your right leg slightly upwards and away from the wall, bringing your knee closer to your chest.

5. Bring the right leg back towards the wall, resting the sole of your feet against it, and repeat the same motion with your left leg.

6. Repeat this exercise, alternating between both legs for at least 8-10 minutes.

Additional Benefits:

- Engages and strengthens the core muscles
- Improves balance and coordination
- Tones the lower abdomen and thighs
- Enhances stability

Worksheet

Reader Check-In! Now that you've gone through a few exercises, stop for a few minutes to breathe and check-in!

Answer the following questions to get a better understanding of how your body works with the exercises in this section!

Name: _____   Date: _____

1. **Experience:**

- How would you rate your overall experience with the Wall Pilates session?

    - ❍ Excellent

    - ❍ Good

    - ❍ Fair

    - ❍ Poor

2. **Instructions:**

- How would you rate the instructions?

    - ❍ Excellent

    - ❍ Good

    - ❍ Fair

    - ❍ Poor

3. **Structure:**

- Was the pace of the instructions appropriate for your fitness level?

    - ❍ Yes

    - ❍ It was complicated

    - ❍ It was too simple

4. Exercise and Difficulty:

- How challenging did you find the exercises?

  - ○ Very challenging
  - ○ Mildly challenging
  - ○ Just right
  - ○ Not challenging enough

- Were the exercises and sequences clearly explained and demonstrated?

  - ○ Yes, very clearly
  - ○ Somewhat clearly
  - ○ Not clearly enough

5. Personal Impact:

- How do you feel physically after the session?

  - ○ Energized and strong
  - ○ Relaxed and balanced
  - ○ No significant change
  - ○ Tired or sore

- How do you feel mentally and emotionally after the session?

  - ○ Balanced and peaceful
  - ○ Positive and uplifted
  - ○ No significant change
  - ○ Stressed or anxious

Did these exercises help you lessen your stress and pain?

_____

_____

_____

Do you see yourself continuing these practices in the future? Why or why not?

_____

_____

_____

Chapter 5: Somatic Exercises for Mind-Body Balance

Somatic exercises are excellent for achieving mind-body balance because they integrate mindful movement with physical exercise to promote overall body harmony. These practices emphasize awareness of bodily sensations and the connection between mental and physical health.

The somatic exercises included in this section involve slow, purposeful movements and deep breathing, which help to calm the mind and center the body. This practice enhances the sense of body position and movement, leading to better coordination and balance. By focusing on each movement and breath, you can achieve mindfulness, which can lessen stress and improve emotional regulation.

These movements require concentration and precise control, promoting a deep connection between the mind and body. The practice enhances muscular alignment and flexibility, aiding in a balanced and stable physical state.

Both somatic yoga and Wall Pilates promote relaxation and reduce tension, which is crucial for achieving mental clarity and physical ease. The emphasis on breathing and mindful awareness in these practices helps to synchronize the mind and body, creating a sense of unity and balance. By regularly practicing these poses, you can develop a deeper understanding of your body and how it respond to stress. This heightened awareness allows for better management of physical and mental stressors, leading to a more balanced life.

Cat-Cow Stretch

Instructions:

1. Take the starting position on your hands and knees. Your wrists should be aligned with your shoulders, and your knees should be aligned with your hips.

2. Inhale deeply, arch your back and drop your belly towards the floor. Lift your head and tailbone towards the ceiling.

3. Hold the pose for at least 10 seconds, and feel the gentle stretch at the front of your torso.

4. Now exhale and curve your spine. Tuck your chin towards your chest and bring your belly button closer to your spine.

5. Press your palms into the ground and round your back towards the ceiling. This will make you look like an angry cat.

6. Hold the pose for at least 10 seconds.

7. Repeat this sequence, switching between Cat and Cow Poses every 10 seconds.

8. Continue doing this for at least 8-10 minutes.

Additional Benefits:

- Enhances spine flexibility and mobility
- Stretches the back, neck, and torso
- Promotes better posture
- Relieves tension in the spine
- Stimulates internal organs

Tree Pose

Instructions:

1. Begin this pose by standing with your arms by your sides and your feet hip-width apart.

2. Put your weight on your left foot and lift your right foot off the ground.

3. Bend your right leg at the knee, and gently bring the sole of your right foot to rest on the inner left thigh. If you feel strain on your muscles while moving your foot to the thigh, you can also rest it on your calf or ankle. Avoid placing your foot directly on the knee joint.

4. Press your foot firmly into your leg and your leg back into your foot; this will create a strong connection.

5. Bring your hands in front of your heart and join the palms.

6. Lengthen your spine, lifting your chest slightly.

7. Hold the pose for at least 3-4 minutes.

8. Repeat the pose on the opposite side.

Additional Benefits:

- Improves balance and stability

- Strengthens the legs, ankles, and feet

- Stretches the hip area

- Stretches the thighs and groin

- Enhances concentration and focus

- Promotes a sense of grounding and calm

Warrior II Pose

Instructions:

1. Begin the pose by standing on your mat with your feet joined together and your arms by your sides.

2. Separate your feet wide apart (approximately 3-4 feet). This distance can be adjusted according to your flexibility and comfort level.

3. The toes of your right foot should be pointing straight, this can be accomplished by turning your right foot to 90 degrees. Bring your right heel in an aligned arch with your left foot.

4. Bend your right knee and bring it directly over your right ankle. Your right thigh should be parallel to the floor, and your knee should not extend past your ankle.

5. Keep your left leg straight, and press your left foot firmly into the mat.

6. Stretch your arms out to the sides. Keep your palms facing up.

7. Keep your head in line with your right arm.

8. Sink deeper towards the floor and put weight on your right hip, feeling a stretch along your inner left thigh.

9. Hold the pose for at least 3-5 minutes.

10. Repeat the pose on the opposite side.

Additional Benefits:

- Strengthens the legs, hips, and shoulders
- Stretches the hips, groin, and chest
- Enhances stamina
- Improves balance and stability
- Promotes a sense of empowerment and focus

Worksheet

Reader Check-In! Now that you've gone through a few exercises, stop for a few minutes to breathe and check-in!

Answer the following questions to get a better understanding of how your body works with the exercises in this section!

Name: _____   Date: _____

1. **Experience:**

   - Excellent

   - Good

   - Fair

   - Poor

2. **Instructions:**

   - Excellent

   - Good

   - Fair

   - Poor

3. **Structure:**

   - Was the pace suitable for your experience?

   - Yes

   - It was complicated

   - It was too simplified

4. **Exercise and Difficulty:**

• How challenging did you find the yoga poses?

  ○ Very challenging

  ○ Mildly challenging

  ○ Just right

  ○ Not challenging enough

5. **Personal Impact:**

• How do you feel physically after the session?

  ○ Energized and refreshed

  ○ Relaxed and calm

  ○ No significant change

  ○ Tired or sore

• How do you feel mentally and emotionally after the session?

  ○ Balanced and peaceful

  ○ Positive and uplifted

  ○ No significant change

  ○ Stressed or anxious

Did these exercises help you lessen your stress and pain?

_____

_____

_____

Do you see yourself continuing these practices in the future? Why or why not?

_____

_____

_____

Wall Supported Side Planks

Instructions:

1. Start the exercise by standing sideways next to a wall. Use your left hand to support your weight as you lean against the wall.

2. Your feet should be further away from the wall than your upper body. Now, raise your right arm towards the ceiling and hold it there for 4-5 seconds.

3. Press firmly into the wall with your left forearm to support your body weight.

4. After 4-5 seconds, raise your right leg to the side, still holding your right arm towards the ceiling. Hold this pose for 4-5 seconds.

5. Bring the sole of your right foot to rest on the inside of your left calf, inhaling and exhaling slowly, and hold this position for 4-5 seconds.

6. Then, slowly lower your right leg to the ground and bring your right hand to rest on your hip. Exhale, holding this pose for 4-5 seconds. Do this for at least 3-5 minutes.

7. Repeat the exercise on the other side, ensuring that your breathing stays calm.

Additional Benefits:

- Strengthens the core and shoulders

- Enhances stability and balance

- Engages the muscles in the legs and glutes

- Supports better posture

Wall Supported Boat Pose

Instructions:

1. Start by sitting on the floor facing on a yoga mat facing towards the wall.

2. Place your hands on the floor beside your hips for stability, inhale, and slowly bring the soles of your feet to rest on the wall. Your body should form an L shape.

3. Extend your arms on both sides with your palms facing each other.

4. Straighten your back and chest. Inhale and hold the pose for at least 10 seconds, maintaining balance.

5. Then, exhale as you return your feet to the floor and return to a seated position.

6. Repeat this exercise for at least 10 minutes.

Additional Benefits:

- Strengthens the core and hips
- Improves balance and stability
- Enhances concentration and focus
- Tones the abdomen muscles
- Supports better posture and spinal alignment

Worksheet

Reader Check-In! Now that you've gone through a few exercises, stop for a few minutes to breathe and check-in!

Answer the following questions to get a better understanding of how your body works with the exercises in this section!

Name: _____   Date: _____

1. **Experience:**

• How would you rate your overall experience with the Wall Pilates session?

   ○ Excellent

   ○ Good

   ○ Fair

   ○ Poor

2. **Instructions:**

• How would you rate the instructions?

   ○ Excellent

   ○ Good

   ○ Fair

   ○ Poor

3. **Structure:**

• Was the pace of the instructions appropriate for your fitness level?

   ○ Yes

   ○ It was complicated

   ○ It was too simple

4. Exercise and Difficulty:

- How challenging did you find the exercises?

  - ○ Very challenging

  - ○ Mildly challenging

  - ○ Just right

  - ○ Not challenging enough

- Were the exercises and sequences clearly explained and demonstrated?

  - ○ Yes, very clearly

  - ○ Somewhat clearly

  - ○ Not clearly enough

5. Personal Impact:

- How do you feel physically after the session?

  - ○ Energized and strong

  - ○ Relaxed and balanced

  - ○ No significant change

  - ○ Tired or sore

- How do you feel mentally and emotionally after the session?

  - ○ Balanced and peaceful

  - ○ Positive and uplifted

  - ○ No significant change

  - ○ Stressed or anxious

Did these exercises help you lessen your stress and pain?

_____

_____

_____

Do you see yourself continuing these practices in the future? Why or why not?

_____

_____

_____

Chapter 6: My 28-Day Focus Plan

An exercise focus plan is crucial for maintaining a healthy body. It provides structure and regularity that supports overall physical and mental well-being. By using these exercises in your somatic exercise routine, you can gain numerous health benefits, for example, good heart health enhanced muscle strength, increased flexibility, better mental health, and greater resilience to stress.

A well-structured weekly exercise plan helps ensure that you engage in a balanced mix of exercises, targeting different areas of fitness. This balance is essential for comprehensive health benefits. For example, flexibility exercises, including yoga or stretching exercises, improved joint mobility and reducing the chance of injuries, muscle strain, stress, etc.

Consistency is key to earning the long-term benefits of somatic exercise. A weekly exercise plan provides a clear schedule, making it easier to stay motivated. By setting specific days and times for your workouts, you create a routine that becomes a regular part of your life. This consistency helps in forming healthy habits, making it less likely that you'll skip workouts.

A focused exercise plan also allows for better progress tracking and setting realistic goals. By planning your somatic exercise routines, you can monitor your improvements over time, whether it's increasing the distance you can run, reducing stress, dealing with trauma, or becoming more flexible. Setting achievable goals keeps you motivated and provides a sense of accomplishment, which can further reinforce your commitment to maintaining a healthy lifestyle.

Moreover, a weekly exercise plan can help prevent the risk of injury. By alternating between yoga and Wall Pilates somatic exercises on different days, you give your body adequate time to rest and recover. This variation not only keeps your workouts interesting but also ensures that different muscles are worked and given time to recover.

Mental health benefits are a significant aspect of maintaining a weekly exercise plan. It is scientifically proven that regular workout routines reduce anxiety and depression, improve mood, and boost overall mental well-being. This is boosted even more with somatic exercises, which are specifically aimed at reducing mental stress. Exercise help release hormones called endorphons. These are your body's natural mood boosters, and helps reduce levels of stress hormones like cortisol. Additionally, having a structured exercise routine can provide a sense of purpose and accomplishment, contributing to better mental health.

A weekly exercise plan encourages mindfulness and self-care. Taking the time to plan and prioritize your workouts shows a commitment to your well-being. It allows you to carve out time in your busy schedule to focus on yourself, promoting a balanced and healthy lifestyle.

This is why the following pages contain a detailed 28-day workout plan, crafted to provide a set schedule and routine that can help you maintain your mental and physical health through somatic movement therapy.

Before You Begin: Keep a few rules in mind before you begin these exercises!

1. Always warm up before starting your exercise routine and cool down afterward with gentle stretches.

2. Adjust the duration and number of sets according to your fitness level and comfort.

3. Listen to your body and modify or skip exercises if you experience any discomfort or pain.

Week 1	
Day 1:	Legs-Up-the-Wall Pose (10 minutes) Child's Pose (10 minutes) Corpse Pose (10 minutes)
Day 2:	Wall Roll Down (10 minutes) Wall Angel (10 minutes) Supine Twist (10 minutes)
Day 3:	High Lunge (10 minutes) Downward-Facing Dog (10 minutes) Wall Squat (10 minutes)
Day 4:	Wall Push-Up (10 minutes) Seated Forward Bend (10 minutes) Supine Bound Angle Pose (10 minutes)
Day 5:	Cobra Pose (10 minutes) Wall Leg Slide (10 minutes) Wall Roll-Up (10 minutes)
Day 6:	Seated Spinal Twist (10 minutes) Extended Triangle Pose (10 minutes) Boat Pose (10 minutes)
Day 7:	Rest or gentle stretching

Week 2

Day 8:	Wall Crunches (10 minutes) Wall Knee Tucks (10 minutes) Cat-Cow Stretch (10 minutes)
Day 9:	Tree Pose (10 minutes) Warrior II Pose (10 minutes) Wall Supported Side Planks (10 minutes)
Day 10:	Wall Supported Boat Pose (10 minutes) Legs-Up-the-Wall Pose (10 minutes) Corpse Pose (10 minutes)
Day 11:	Wall Roll Down (10 minutes) Wall Angel (10 minutes) Supine Twist (10 minutes)
Day 12:	High Lunge (10 minutes) Downward-Facing Dog (10 minutes) Wall Squat (10 minutes)
Day 13:	Wall Push-Up (10 minutes) Seated Forward Bend (10 minutes) Supine Bound Angle Pose (10 minutes)
Day 14:	Rest or gentle stretching

Week 3

Day 15:	Cobra Pose (10 minutes) Wall Leg Slide (10 minutes) Wall Roll-Up (10 minutes)
Day 16:	Seated Spinal Twist (10 minutes) Extended Triangle Pose (10 minutes) Boat Pose (10 minutes)
Day 17:	Wall Crunches (10 minutes) Wall Knee Tucks (10 minutes) Cat-Cow Stretch (10 minutes)
Day 18:	Tree Pose (10 minutes) Warrior II Pose (10 minutes) Wall Supported Side Planks (10 minutes)
Day 19:	Wall Supported Boat Pose (10 minutes) Legs-Up-the-Wall Pose (10 minutes) Corpse Pose (10 minutes)
Day 20:	Wall Roll Down (10 minutes) Wall Angel (10 minutes) Supine Twist (10 minutes)
Day 21:	Rest or gentle stretching

Week 4

Day 22:	High Lunge (10 minutes) Downward-Facing Dog (10 minutes) Wall Squat (10 minutes)
Day 23:	Wall Push-Up (10 minutes) Seated Forward Bend (10 minutes) Supine Bound Angle Pose (10 minutes)
Day 24:	Cobra Pose (10 minutes) Wall Leg Slide (10 minutes) Wall Roll-Up (10 minutes)
Day 25:	Seated Spinal Twist (10 minutes) Extended Triangle Pose (10 minutes) Boat Pose (10 minutes)
Day 26:	Wall Crunches (10 minutes) Wall Knee Tucks (10 minutes) Cat-Cow Stretch (10 minutes)
Day 27:	Tree Pose (10 minutes) Warrior II Pose (10 minutes) Wall Supported Side Planks (10 minutes)
Day 28:	Wall Supported Boat Pose (10 minutes) Legs-Up-the-Wall Pose (10 minutes) Corpse Pose (10 minutes)

Worksheet

Use the given templates to track your progress. This will help you keep up with the self-care and stay healthy!

Week 1	Week 2	Week 3	Week 4
☐ ☐ ☐ ☐ ☐ ☐ ☐	☐ ☐ ☐ ☐ ☐ ☐ ☐	☐ ☐ ☐ ☐ ☐ ☐ ☐	☐ ☐ ☐ ☐ ☐ ☐ ☐
☐ ☐ ☐ ☐ ☐ ☐ ☐	☐ ☐ ☐ ☐ ☐ ☐ ☐	☐ ☐ ☐ ☐ ☐ ☐ ☐	☐ ☐ ☐ ☐ ☐ ☐ ☐
☐ ☐ ☐ ☐ ☐ ☐ ☐	☐ ☐ ☐ ☐ ☐ ☐ ☐	☐ ☐ ☐ ☐ ☐ ☐ ☐	☐ ☐ ☐ ☐ ☐ ☐ ☐
☐ ☐ ☐ ☐ ☐ ☐ ☐	☐ ☐ ☐ ☐ ☐ ☐ ☐	☐ ☐ ☐ ☐ ☐ ☐ ☐	☐ ☐ ☐ ☐ ☐ ☐ ☐
☐ ☐ ☐ ☐ ☐ ☐ ☐	☐ ☐ ☐ ☐ ☐ ☐ ☐	☐ ☐ ☐ ☐ ☐ ☐ ☐	☐ ☐ ☐ ☐ ☐ ☐ ☐
☐ ☐ ☐ ☐ ☐ ☐ ☐	☐ ☐ ☐ ☐ ☐ ☐ ☐	☐ ☐ ☐ ☐ ☐ ☐ ☐	☐ ☐ ☐ ☐ ☐ ☐ ☐
☐ ☐ ☐ ☐ ☐ ☐ ☐	☐ ☐ ☐ ☐ ☐ ☐ ☐	☐ ☐ ☐ ☐ ☐ ☐ ☐	☐ ☐ ☐ ☐ ☐ ☐ ☐
☐ ☐ ☐ ☐ ☐ ☐ ☐	☐ ☐ ☐ ☐ ☐ ☐ ☐	☐ ☐ ☐ ☐ ☐ ☐ ☐	☐ ☐ ☐ ☐ ☐ ☐ ☐
☐ ☐ ☐ ☐ ☐ ☐ ☐	☐ ☐ ☐ ☐ ☐ ☐ ☐	☐ ☐ ☐ ☐ ☐ ☐ ☐	☐ ☐ ☐ ☐ ☐ ☐ ☐
☐ ☐ ☐ ☐ ☐ ☐ ☐	☐ ☐ ☐ ☐ ☐ ☐ ☐	☐ ☐ ☐ ☐ ☐ ☐ ☐	☐ ☐ ☐ ☐ ☐ ☐ ☐
☐ ☐ ☐ ☐ ☐ ☐ ☐	☐ ☐ ☐ ☐ ☐ ☐ ☐	☐ ☐ ☐ ☐ ☐ ☐ ☐	☐ ☐ ☐ ☐ ☐ ☐ ☐
☐ ☐ ☐ ☐ ☐ ☐ ☐	☐ ☐ ☐ ☐ ☐ ☐ ☐	☐ ☐ ☐ ☐ ☐ ☐ ☐	☐ ☐ ☐ ☐ ☐ ☐ ☐
☐ ☐ ☐ ☐ ☐ ☐ ☐	☐ ☐ ☐ ☐ ☐ ☐ ☐	☐ ☐ ☐ ☐ ☐ ☐ ☐	☐ ☐ ☐ ☐ ☐ ☐ ☐
☐ ☐ ☐ ☐ ☐ ☐ ☐	☐ ☐ ☐ ☐ ☐ ☐ ☐	☐ ☐ ☐ ☐ ☐ ☐ ☐	☐ ☐ ☐ ☐ ☐ ☐ ☐
☐ ☐ ☐ ☐ ☐ ☐ ☐	☐ ☐ ☐ ☐ ☐ ☐ ☐	☐ ☐ ☐ ☐ ☐ ☐ ☐	☐ ☐ ☐ ☐ ☐ ☐ ☐
☐ ☐ ☐ ☐ ☐ ☐ ☐	☐ ☐ ☐ ☐ ☐ ☐ ☐	☐ ☐ ☐ ☐ ☐ ☐ ☐	☐ ☐ ☐ ☐ ☐ ☐ ☐

Reflections Worksheet 1

This reflection worksheet is designed to help you assess your experience with somatic exercises, including yoga and Wall Pilates. Take a few moments to reflect on everything you have learned:

Name: _____   Date: _____

Describe your experience with the exercise sessions.

_____

_____

_____

_____

What benefits have you noticed from practicing somatic exercises?

_____

_____

_____

_____

What challenges did you encounter during your somatic exercises practice?

_____

_____

_____

How did you overcome these challenges?

_____

_____

_____

_____

What are your future goals for your somatic exercises?

_____

_____

_____

_____

Intention Setting Worksheet 1

Congratulations on completing your 28-day somatic yoga and somatic wall pilates exercise routine! Setting intentions can help you maintain the benefits you have achieved. Use this worksheet to reflect on your journey and set meaningful intentions for your future practice.

Name: _____   Date: _____

Reflection on the Past 28 Days

What are the key achievements and benefits you've experienced over the past 28 days?

_____

_____

_____

What challenges did you face, and how did you overcome them?

_____

_____

_____

How have you grown personally, physically, and mentally through this practice?

_____

_____

_____

Setting Future Intentions:

What are your future physical fitness goals?

_____

_____

_____

What mental and emotional goals do you wish to achieve?

_____

_____

_____

How do you plan to integrate somatic yoga and Wall Pilates into your regular routine?

_____

_____

_____

Describe your long-term vision for your health and well-being.

_____

_____

_____

What daily practices will support your intentions?

_____

_____

_____

How will you incorporate mindfulness into your daily life?

_____

_____

_____

Who can support you in achieving your intentions?

_____

_____

_____

Commitment:

Write a personal affirmation that will inspire and motivate you to stay committed to your practice.

_____

_____

_____

Outline a simple action plan for the next month to help you stay on track.

_____

_____

_____

Chapter 7: Nutrient-Rich Recipes to Fuel and Enhance Mind-Body Awareness

Maintaining a healthy diet is crucial in supporting somatic yoga and Wall Pilates for a strong mind-body connection and overall physical well-being. The food you consume directly affects your body, supplying the essential energy and nutrients needed for ideal performance. A balanced diet should contain of various food groups, including fruits, vegetables, whole grains and lean proteins, these only support bodily functions but also enhance mental clarity and emotional stability. When combined with physical practices like somatic yoga and Wall Pilates, which emphasize mindful movement and body awareness, a nutritious diet increases the benefits of these exercises. This collaboration leads to better energy levels, improved concentration, and quicker recovery times.

Somatic exercises integrate physical movement with mental focus, developing a deeper connection between the mind and body. These practices help release tension, increase flexibility, and build strength, all of which demand proper nourishment from a healthy diet. Consuming nutrient-rich foods ensures that practitioners have the energy required to engage fully in these exercises, making the most of their benefits. A diet high in antioxidants, vitamins, and minerals supports the body's healing processes, reducing inflammation and aiding in the repair of muscles stressed during exercise.

The mind-body connection highlighted in somatic therapy is further strengthened by a diet that promotes brain health. Foods rich in omega-3 fatty acids, such as fish and flax seeds, aid with this. These are known to enhance cognitive function and emotional well-being. Similarly, complex carbohydrates from whole grains provide a source of glucose, which is the brain's primary fuel, helping in mental focus and stability. By following a healthy diet, you can ensure that your body and mind are well-prepared to meet the demands of daily life and your somatic practices, these will lead you to a more balanced state of mind.

The diet plan given in the following pages will help you achieve a perfectly healthy mindset by enhancing your mind-body connection through the nutrients you consume.

Week 1

Day 1:

- **Breakfast:** Greek yogurt with honey, chia seeds, and mixed berries
- **Lunch:** Quinoa salad with chickpeas, cucumber, tomatoes, and lemon-tahini dressing
- **Snack:** Apple slices with almond butter
- **Dinner:** Grilled salmon with roasted sweet potatoes and steamed broccoli

Day 2:

- **Breakfast:** Oatmeal topped with banana slices and a sprinkle of flax seeds
- **Lunch:** Turkey and avocado wrap with whole grain tortilla
- **Snack:** Carrot sticks with hummus
- **Dinner:** Stir-fried tofu with mixed vegetables and brown rice

Day 3:

- **Breakfast:** Smoothie with spinach, banana, almond milk, and protein powder
- **Lunch:** Lentil soup with a side of mixed green salad
- **Snack:** Handful of nuts and dried fruit
- **Dinner:** Baked chicken breast with quinoa and roasted Brussels sprouts

Day 4:

- **Breakfast:** Whole grain toast with avocado and poached eggs
- **Lunch:** Greek salad with olives, feta, cucumbers, and tomatoes
- **Snack:** Cottage cheese with pineapple chunks
- **Dinner:** Shrimp stir-fry with vegetables and wild rice

Day 5:

- **Breakfast:** Chia pudding made with almond milk and topped with fresh berries
- **Lunch:** Grilled chicken Caesar salad
- **Snack:** Celery sticks with peanut butter
- **Dinner:** Baked cod with a side of couscous and steamed green beans

Day 6:

- **Breakfast:** Smoothie bowl with mixed fruits, granola, and a drizzle of honey
- **Lunch:** Veggie wrap with hummus, spinach, bell peppers, and carrots
- **Snack:** Greek yogurt with a handful of walnuts
- **Dinner:** Turkey chili with kidney beans and a side of cornbread

Day 7:

- **Breakfast:** Scrambled eggs with spinach and whole-grain toast
- **Lunch:** Mixed bean salad with corn, bell peppers, and a cilantro-lime dressing
- **Snack:** Pear slices with cheese
- **Dinner:** Grilled vegetable kebabs with a side of brown rice

Week 2

Day 8:

- **Breakfast:** Overnight oats with almond milk, chia seeds, and strawberries
- **Lunch:** Chicken and avocado salad with mixed greens
- **Snack:** Sliced bell peppers with guacamole
- **Dinner:** Baked salmon with quinoa and roasted asparagus

Day 9:

- **Breakfast:** Greek yogurt parfait with granola and blueberries
- **Lunch:** Quinoa bowl with black beans, corn, avocado, and salsa
- **Snack:** Apple with almond butter
- **Dinner:** Grilled shrimp with couscous and steamed broccoli

Day 10:

- **Breakfast:** Smoothie with spinach, banana, almond milk, and flax seeds
- **Lunch:** Lentil and vegetable soup with a side salad
- **Snack:** Handful of mixed nuts
- **Dinner:** Baked chicken with roasted sweet potatoes and green beans

Day 11:

- **Breakfast:** Whole grain toast with avocado and boiled eggs
- **Lunch:** Greek salad with olives, feta, cucumbers, and tomatoes
- **Snack:** Cottage cheese with sliced peaches
- **Dinner:** Stir-fried tofu with vegetables and brown rice

Day 12:

- **Breakfast:** Chia seed pudding with almond milk and fresh berries
- **Lunch:** Turkey and spinach wrap with whole grain tortilla
- **Snack:** Carrot sticks with hummus
- **Dinner:** Grilled salmon with wild rice and steamed green beans

Day 13:

- **Breakfast:** Smoothie bowl with mixed fruits, granola, and a drizzle of honey
- **Lunch:** Veggie wrap with hummus, spinach, bell peppers, and carrots
- **Snack:** Greek yogurt with walnuts
- **Dinner:** Turkey chili with kidney beans and a side of cornbread

Day 14:

- **Breakfast:** Scrambled eggs with spinach and whole-grain toast
- **Lunch:** Mixed bean salad with corn, bell peppers, and a cilantro-lime dressing
- **Snack:** Sliced pears with cheese
- **Dinner:** Grilled vegetable kebabs with a side of brown rice

Week 3

Day 15:

- **Breakfast:** Overnight oats with almond milk, chia seeds, and strawberries
- **Lunch:** Chicken and avocado salad with mixed greens
- **Snack:** Sliced bell peppers with guacamole
- **Dinner:** Baked salmon with quinoa and roasted asparagus

Day 16:

- **Breakfast:** Greek yogurt parfait with granola and blueberries
- **Lunch:** Quinoa bowl with black beans, corn, avocado, and salsa
- **Snack:** Apple with almond butter
- **Dinner:** Grilled shrimp with couscous and steamed broccoli

Day 17:

- **Breakfast:** Smoothie with spinach, banana, almond milk, and flax seeds
- **Lunch:** Lentil and vegetable soup with a side salad
- **Snack:** Handful of mixed nuts
- **Dinner:** Baked chicken with roasted sweet potatoes and green beans

Day 18:

- **Breakfast:** Whole grain toast with avocado and boiled eggs
- **Lunch:** Greek salad with olives, feta, cucumbers, and tomatoes
- **Snack:** Cottage cheese with sliced peaches
- **Dinner:** Stir-fried tofu with vegetables and brown rice

Day 19:

- **Breakfast:** Chia seed pudding with almond milk and fresh berries
- **Lunch:** Turkey and spinach wrap with whole grain tortilla
- **Snack:** Carrot sticks with hummus
- **Dinner:** Grilled salmon with wild rice and steamed green beans

Day 20:

- **Breakfast:** Smoothie bowl with mixed fruits, granola, and a drizzle of honey
- **Lunch:** Veggie wrap with hummus, spinach, bell peppers, and carrots
- **Snack:** Greek yogurt with walnuts
- **Dinner:** Turkey chili with kidney beans and a side of cornbread

Day 21:

- **Breakfast:** Scrambled eggs with spinach and whole-grain toast
- **Lunch:** Mixed bean salad with corn, bell peppers, and a cilantro-lime dressing
- **Snack:** Sliced pears with cheese
- **Dinner:** Grilled vegetable kebabs with a side of brown rice

Week 4

Day 22:

- **Breakfast:** Overnight oats with almond milk, chia seeds, and strawberries
- **Lunch:** Chicken and avocado salad with mixed greens
- **Snack:** Sliced bell peppers with guacamole
- **Dinner:** Baked salmon with quinoa and roasted asparagus

Day 23:

- **Breakfast:** Greek yogurt parfait with granola and blueberries
- **Lunch:** Quinoa bowl with black beans, corn, avocado, and salsa
- **Snack:** Apple with almond butter
- **Dinner:** Grilled shrimp with couscous and steamed broccoli

Day 24:

- **Breakfast:** Smoothie with spinach, banana, almond milk, and flax seeds
- **Lunch:** Lentil and vegetable soup with a side salad
- **Snack:** Handful of mixed nuts
- **Dinner:** Baked chicken with roasted sweet potatoes and green beans

Day 25:

- **Breakfast:** Whole grain toast with avocado and boiled eggs
- **Lunch:** Greek salad with olives, feta, cucumbers, and tomatoes
- **Snack:** Cottage cheese with sliced peaches
- **Dinner:** Stir-fried tofu with vegetables and brown rice

Day 26:

- **Breakfast:** Chia seed pudding with almond milk and fresh berries
- **Lunch:** Turkey and spinach wrap with whole grain tortilla
- **Snack:** Carrot sticks with hummus
- **Dinner:** Grilled salmon with wild rice and steamed green beans

Day 27:

- **Breakfast:** Smoothie bowl with mixed fruits, granola, and a drizzle of honey
- **Lunch:** Veggie wrap with hummus, spinach, bell peppers, and carrots
- **Snack:** Greek yogurt with walnuts
- **Dinner:** Turkey chili with kidney beans and a side of cornbread

Day 28:

- **Breakfast:** Scrambled eggs with spinach and whole-grain toast
- **Lunch:** Mixed bean salad with corn, bell peppers, and a cilantro-lime dressing
- **Snack:** Sliced pears with cheese
- **Dinner:** Grilled vegetable kebabs with a side of brown rice

Additional Tips:

- Drink plenty of water throughout the day.
- Include herbal teas or infused water for hydration.
- Avoid processed foods and sugary snacks.
- Ensure a balance of macronutrients: carbohydrates, proteins, and fats.
- Listen to your body and adjust portion sizes based on your hunger and energy levels.
- Incorporate plenty of colorful fruits and vegetables for vitamins and minerals.

Reflections Worksheet 2

This reflection worksheet is designed to help you assess your experience with somatic exercises, including yoga, Wall Pilates, and following a proper diet plan. Take a few moments to reflect on everything you have learned:

Name: _____   Date: _____

How would you describe your experience following the diet plan?

_____

_____

_____

_____

What positive changes have you noticed in your health and well-being?

_____

_____

_____

_____

What challenges did you face while following the diet plan?

_____

_____

_____

_____

How did you adapt to these challenges?

_____

_____

_____

_____

What are your future goals for your dietary habits?

_____

_____

_____

_____

How have somatic yoga, Wall Pilates, and a proper diet plan complemented each other in your routine?

_____

_____

_____

How have these practices collectively contributed to your personal growth and overall well-being?

_____

_____

_____

Chapter 8: Your Weekly Self-Care Guide

Self-care is an essential component of somatic exercises, as it plays a crucial role in developing a healthy mindset. While somatic practices focus on the mind-body connection through mindful movement and physical awareness, self-care extends this approach by addressing emotional, mental, and social health. Together, they form a complete strategy for maintaining balance and enhancing quality of life.

Engaging in regular self-care practices, such as satisfactory sleep, proper nutrition, and stress management, provides the groundwork necessary for somatic exercises to be most effective. For example, proper sleep ensures that the body is rested and capable of performing physical activities without strain. Eating a balanced diet fuels the body and supplies the necessary nutrients to support energy levels and muscle recovery, which are vital for maintaining an active lifestyle.

Beyond physical health, self-care practices like mindfulness meditation, journaling, and spending time in nature contribute to emotional resilience and mental clarity. These activities help to reduce stress and anxiety, and create a mental state that is more open to the benefits of somatic exercises. When the mind is calm and focused, you can engage more deeply with somatic practice, enhancing the mind-body connection and achieving better results.

Social self-care, such as maintaining healthy relationships and seeking support from friends and family, provides emotional stability and a sense of community. This support system can motivate you to stay committed to your somatic exercise routine and provide encouragement during challenging times.

Incorporating self-care into daily life ensures that you are not only physically prepared for somatic exercises but also mentally and emotionally balanced. This holistic approach to health increases the benefits of somatic practices and leads to a more fulfilling life. By prioritizing self-care alongside somatic exercises, you can achieve a workable approach to health that nurtures both the body and the mind.

The following pages contain a variety of self-love and self-care exercises that you can practice alongside your 28-day meal plan to foster better physical and mental health.

Week 1: Mindfulness and Mental Health

Day 1: Journaling

- Spend 15 minutes writing about your thoughts, feelings, and experiences. Reflect on what you're grateful for and set a positive intention for the day.

Day 2: Digital Detox

- Disconnect from all screens and social media platforms for at least two hours. Use this time for a hobby, read a book, or take a walk.

Day 3: Meditation

- Practice a guided meditation for 10-15 minutes. Focus on your breathing and let go of any stress or worries.

Day 4: Nature Walk

- Take a walk in a natural setting. Pay attention to the sounds, smells, and sights around you.

Day 5: Gratitude List

- Write down five things you are grateful for today. Reflect on how these things enhance your life.

Day 6: Positive Affirmations

- Write and repeat three positive affirmations to boost your self-esteem and outlook.

Day 7: Creative Expression

- Spend time doing something creative, like drawing or painting. Allow yourself to express your emotions through art.

Week 2: Physical Wellness

Day 8: Hydration Focus

- Drink at least eight glasses of water today. Notice how staying hydrated makes you feel.

Day 9: Healthy Eating

- Prepare a nutritious meal with vegetables and lean proteins. Enjoy the process of cooking and eating mindfully.

Day 10: Dance Session

- Follow a beginner dance routine to stretch your body and let go of your worries.

Day 11: Sleep Hygiene

- Create a bedtime routine. Turn off electronics an hour before bed, read a book, and try to get eight hours of sleep.

Day 12: Stretching Routine

- Perform a full-body stretching routine to relieve tension and improve flexibility.

Day 13: Mindful Eating

- Eat a meal slowly and without distractions. Pay attention to the flavors and textures.

Day 14: Outdoor Activity

- Engage in an outdoor activity like cycling, hiking, or gardening. Enjoy the fresh air and physical movement.

Week 3: Emotional and Social Wellness

Day 15: Connect with a Friend

- Reach out to a friend or family member. Have a meaningful conversation and strengthen your social connections.

Day 16: Acts of Kindness

- Perform a random act of kindness. It could be something small, like complimenting someone or helping a neighbor.

Day 17: Self-Love

- Write a letter to yourself expressing kindness and understanding. Acknowledge your strengths and forgive your imperfections.

Day 18: Music Therapy

- Listen to your favorite music or explore new genres. Notice how different tunes affect your mood.

Day 19: Emotional Release

- Engage in an activity that allows you to release emotions, such as singing or writing.

Day 20: Pet Therapy

- Spend time with a pet or visit an animal shelter. Enjoy the unconditional love of animals.

Day 21: Volunteer

- Volunteer your time. Helping others can boost your sense of well-being.

Week 4: Personal Growth and Reflection

Day 22: Learn Something New

- Take a short online course or read about a topic that interests you. Challenge your mind and expand your knowledge.

Day 23: De-clutter

- Spend time de-cluttering a part of your home. Create a clean and organized space to enhance your mental clarity.

Day 24: Goal Setting

- Write down three short-term and three long-term goals. Plan steps to achieve them.

Day 25: Reflection

- Reflect on the past month. Write about your accomplishments, challenges, and what you've learned about yourself.

Day 26: Visualization

- Practice a visualization exercise. Imagine your future self, achieving your goals and living a fulfilling life.

Day 27: Revisit Gratitude

- Review your gratitude list from Day 5. Add new items and reflect on how your perspective has shifted.

Day 28: Self-Care Celebration

- Celebrate completing the challenge by treating yourself to something special, like a relaxing bath, a favorite meal, or a small gift.

Additional Tips:

- Stay consistent and patient with your self-care.

- Customize the challenge to fit your likings and needs.

- Encourage a friend or family member to join you for motivation.

- Track your progress and note any positive changes in your well-being.

Worksheet

Use the given templates to track your progress. This will help you keep up with the self-care and stay healthy!

Week 1	Week 2	Week 3	Week 4
☐ ☐ ☐ ☐ ☐ ☐ ☐	☐ ☐ ☐ ☐ ☐ ☐ ☐	☐ ☐ ☐ ☐ ☐ ☐ ☐	☐ ☐ ☐ ☐ ☐ ☐ ☐
☐ ☐ ☐ ☐ ☐ ☐ ☐	☐ ☐ ☐ ☐ ☐ ☐ ☐	☐ ☐ ☐ ☐ ☐ ☐ ☐	☐ ☐ ☐ ☐ ☐ ☐ ☐
☐ ☐ ☐ ☐ ☐ ☐ ☐	☐ ☐ ☐ ☐ ☐ ☐ ☐	☐ ☐ ☐ ☐ ☐ ☐ ☐	☐ ☐ ☐ ☐ ☐ ☐ ☐
☐ ☐ ☐ ☐ ☐ ☐ ☐	☐ ☐ ☐ ☐ ☐ ☐ ☐	☐ ☐ ☐ ☐ ☐ ☐ ☐	☐ ☐ ☐ ☐ ☐ ☐ ☐
☐ ☐ ☐ ☐ ☐ ☐ ☐	☐ ☐ ☐ ☐ ☐ ☐ ☐	☐ ☐ ☐ ☐ ☐ ☐ ☐	☐ ☐ ☐ ☐ ☐ ☐ ☐
☐ ☐ ☐ ☐ ☐ ☐ ☐	☐ ☐ ☐ ☐ ☐ ☐ ☐	☐ ☐ ☐ ☐ ☐ ☐ ☐	☐ ☐ ☐ ☐ ☐ ☐ ☐
☐ ☐ ☐ ☐ ☐ ☐ ☐	☐ ☐ ☐ ☐ ☐ ☐ ☐	☐ ☐ ☐ ☐ ☐ ☐ ☐	☐ ☐ ☐ ☐ ☐ ☐ ☐
☐ ☐ ☐ ☐ ☐ ☐ ☐	☐ ☐ ☐ ☐ ☐ ☐ ☐	☐ ☐ ☐ ☐ ☐ ☐ ☐	☐ ☐ ☐ ☐ ☐ ☐ ☐
☐ ☐ ☐ ☐ ☐ ☐ ☐	☐ ☐ ☐ ☐ ☐ ☐ ☐	☐ ☐ ☐ ☐ ☐ ☐ ☐	☐ ☐ ☐ ☐ ☐ ☐ ☐
☐ ☐ ☐ ☐ ☐ ☐ ☐	☐ ☐ ☐ ☐ ☐ ☐ ☐	☐ ☐ ☐ ☐ ☐ ☐ ☐	☐ ☐ ☐ ☐ ☐ ☐ ☐
☐ ☐ ☐ ☐ ☐ ☐ ☐	☐ ☐ ☐ ☐ ☐ ☐ ☐	☐ ☐ ☐ ☐ ☐ ☐ ☐	☐ ☐ ☐ ☐ ☐ ☐ ☐
☐ ☐ ☐ ☐ ☐ ☐ ☐	☐ ☐ ☐ ☐ ☐ ☐ ☐	☐ ☐ ☐ ☐ ☐ ☐ ☐	☐ ☐ ☐ ☐ ☐ ☐ ☐
☐ ☐ ☐ ☐ ☐ ☐ ☐	☐ ☐ ☐ ☐ ☐ ☐ ☐	☐ ☐ ☐ ☐ ☐ ☐ ☐	☐ ☐ ☐ ☐ ☐ ☐ ☐
☐ ☐ ☐ ☐ ☐ ☐ ☐	☐ ☐ ☐ ☐ ☐ ☐ ☐	☐ ☐ ☐ ☐ ☐ ☐ ☐	☐ ☐ ☐ ☐ ☐ ☐ ☐
☐ ☐ ☐ ☐ ☐ ☐ ☐	☐ ☐ ☐ ☐ ☐ ☐ ☐	☐ ☐ ☐ ☐ ☐ ☐ ☐	☐ ☐ ☐ ☐ ☐ ☐ ☐
☐ ☐ ☐ ☐ ☐ ☐ ☐	☐ ☐ ☐ ☐ ☐ ☐ ☐	☐ ☐ ☐ ☐ ☐ ☐ ☐	☐ ☐ ☐ ☐ ☐ ☐ ☐
☐ ☐ ☐ ☐ ☐ ☐ ☐	☐ ☐ ☐ ☐ ☐ ☐ ☐	☐ ☐ ☐ ☐ ☐ ☐ ☐	☐ ☐ ☐ ☐ ☐ ☐ ☐

Intention Setting Worksheet 2

Taking time to focus on self-care and self-love is essential for overall well-being. Use this worksheet to reflect on your journey and set meaningful intentions for your future practice.

Name: _____   Date: _____

What are the achievements and benefits you've experienced through your self-care and self-love practices?

_____

_____

_____

_____

What challenges did you face, and how did you overcome them?

_____

_____

_____

How have you grown personally, emotionally, and mentally through these practices?

_____

_____

_____

What are your future physical fitness goals?

_____

_____

_____

_____

What mental goals do you wish to achieve?

_____

_____

_____

_____

How do you plan to integrate self-care and self-love practices into your regular routine?

_____

_____

_____

Describe your long-term vision for your emotional and mental well-being.

_____

_____

_____

Who can support you in achieving your intentions? (e.g., friends, family, therapists)

_____

_____

_____

_____

Commitment:

Write a personal affirmation that will inspire and motivate you to stay committed to your self-care and self-love practices.

_____

_____

_____

Outline a simple action plan for the next month to help you stay on track.

_____

_____

_____

Reflect on what you are grateful for in your self-care and self-love journey.

_____

_____

_____

Creative Expression Integration Worksheet Check-In

The last step in your healing journey, which will let you evaluate your progress clearly, is check-in for the creative expression integration worksheet, which you filled out on page number 26.

Reflect on your feelings, emotions, and physical health. Do you still see yourself in the same light?

_____

_____

_____

Why or why not?

_____

_____

_____

If yes, then what other practices can you adopt to fix this?

_____

_____

_____

Conclusion

This book serves as a comprehensive guide for anyone looking to improve their overall well-being. It offers readers a way to enhance their physical fitness, flexibility, and strength through a mix of somatic therapy and somatic exercises such as yoga and Wall Pilates. The inclusion of a tailored nutrition guide further supports these physical practices, ensuring that your body receives the nourishment it needs to thrive.

What sets this book apart is its holistic approach. It doesn't just focus on physical exercises; it also includes practical tools for mental and emotional health. The reflective activities and worksheets encourage a deeper connection with oneself, creating a greater sense of self-awareness and growth. These elements work together to create a balanced routine that nurtures both body and mind.

With step-by-step instructions and additional benefits throughout the book, you can improve your physical and mental health. Whether you are new to these practices or looking to deepen your current routine, this book provides valuable insights and guidance. By integrating these practices into your daily life, you can achieve a more balanced and fulfilling lifestyle. It's more than just an exercise guide; it's a map to a healthier and happier you.

About the Author

Eva Greenleaf is a trained wellness expert with over two decades of experience in yoga and Wall Pilates. Her journey began as a personal quest for balance and well-being, which evolved into a passionate career dedicated to helping others achieve the same.

Eva has taught countless classes and workshops. Her approach is deeply rooted in the belief that physical health cannot be separated from mental and emotional wellness. This philosophy is apparent in her teaching style, which combines the mindful movement of somatic therapy with thoughtful reflection and self-care practices.

In addition to her teaching experience, Eva holds a degree in nutrition. She has worked with a diverse range of clients, making nutrition and exercise plans to meet individual needs and goals.

This book reflects Eva's approach, offering readers practical tools and guidance for a balanced lifestyle. Through her clear instructions and advice, Eva invites readers to come along on a journey towards greater health and happiness.

Printed in Great Britain
by Amazon

46332165R00084